# Amusement Park Physics

## Published by American Association of Physics Teachers

Amusement Park Physics Handbook Committee

Carole Escobar, *Editor*

**Members of the *Amusement Park Physics* Handbook Committee:**

Carole A. Escobar, Long Island, New York, *Editor*
Ann Brandon, Chicago Heights, Illinois
Ronald De Fronzo, Pawtucket, Rhode Island
Harold Lefcourt, Rockaway, New Jersey
Virginia Moore, Vernon, New Jersey
Barbara Wolff, Maplewood, New Jersey

Published by:
American Association of Physics Teachers
One Physics Ellipse
College Park, MD 20740-3845
U.S.A.

Cover: The cover photo is the "Steamin' Demon" roller coaster from The Great Escape Theme Park in Lake George, New York. Photo courtesy of Ed Lewi Associates, Latham, New York.

# Table of Contents

# Preface

The impetus for this handbook was a workshop given at the 1986 American Association of Physics Teachers (AAPT) Summer Meeting held in Columbus, Ohio. A wealth of materials was provided to participants; Harold Lefcourt was asked by the AAPT Committee on Physics in High Schools to develop them into a publication. Our first meeting as the Amusement Park Physics Handbook Committee was held at Cornell University, immediately following the 1988 AAPT Summer Meeting. The Physics Teaching Resource Agents program found funding for a two-day working session that proved to be extremely fruitful.

At the initial meeting, a subset of the Handbook Committee under the leadership of Nathan Unterman redesigned and refined plans for two accelerometers. PASCO scientific made the accelerometers available in kits and also gave the Committee a travel grant, administered by AAPT, so that we could gather at the 1989 Winter Meeting in San Francisco and begin to test this handbook. We are grateful for this support. Furthermore, in an extraordinary initiative, PASCO has always donated a portion of the proceeds from the sale of the accelerometer kits to the AAPT Committee on Physics in High Schools.

As for the materials themselves, they are the distillation of the work of numerous teachers. In many sections of the book, we have built on the ideas of teachers from all over the country. We would especially like to thank John McGehee for his generous gift of the majority of the material in the measurement section, Don Rathjen for providing us with the California teachers' videotape and for helping with the workshops that we conducted in his state, Clarence Bakken for the overhead masters and helpful criticism, and Carl Duzen for inspiration.

Much of the material is original. In particular, several of the problem sets came from Barbara Wolff and her colleague Klara Samuels. Virginia Moore oversaw the development of a database of resource people during the development of this handbook.

The manuscript has been through four revisions. In this final version, we have incorporated suggestions and corrections made by several hundred teachers who tested the draft editions in our workshops. Their aid and enthusiasm has been most encouraging.

I have relied on two friends—Mario Iona, Professor Emeritus of the University of Denver, and Clifford Swartz, Professor at the State University of New York, Stony Brook—to check the physics, especially in the section on the theory of accelerometers. It is amazing how subtle and familiar physics can suddenly become. Trying to be precise about basic concepts is very much like trying to diaper a greased baby. Every time I thought I had cornered a concept, it would elude my grasp. The tighter I tried to tack down point A, the faster point B escaped me. Professors Iona and Swartz both have my profound gratitude. Both read the work in progress. If errors have crept into this final version, they are mine alone and should be brought to my attention.

*Carole Escobar*, Editor

# Introduction

Physics teachers have been using amusement parks as laboratories for at least two decades. The earliest report in print is John Roeder's 1975 article in *The Physics Teacher,* but a teacher on Long Island told me that he took students to Rye Playland over twenty years ago, and he was not the only one to do so at the time.

Since 1985 there has been a virtual explosion of interest in amusement parks. The San Francisco Exploratorium devoted an entire issue of its publication *Exploratorium Quarterly* to amusement parks in 1987, and even *Money* magazine ran an article on amusement parks which included some physics.

In 1993 student attendance at Physics Days across the country ran to the tens of thousands. In California alone, 10,000 students attended Great America on a single day. Students numbering 15,000 went to Great Adventure in New Jersey, and more than 6,000 went to Valleyfair in Minnesota, and 5,000 to Riverside Park in Massachusetts. Teachers and students may travel several hours each way, as mine do, but there is a teacher in Texas for whom the nearest park is an annual overnight trip.

Accompanying the expansion in interest has been an avalanche of educational materials written and circulated by individual teachers. Members of the AAPT's Amusement Park Physics Handbook Committee collected several hundred pounds of student workbooks from a multitude of teacher groups that were organizing Physics Days at local parks. Carolyn Sumners was a seminal influence with her Informal Science Study, financed by the National Science Foundation. Every student workbook we saw had at least one of her activities, illustrations, or actual pages. She made it clear that students can learn physics by taking measurements and by experiencing the rides.

At first, the amusement park may seem to be an odd place to do serious work. It is designed for fun and excitement, not study. Yet teachers have come to see it as a natural extension of the classroom. The physics of the rides is the basic stuff of a first-year course. Roller coasters demonstrate the conversion of gravitational potential into kinetic energy, rotating swing rides illustrate the vector addition of forces, rotating rides of all sorts allow for computation of centripetal accelerations, and all of those terrifying falls let the students experience free fall. Having first-hand experience with the forces that come into play helps the students to build an intellectual understanding of the principles behind them. Students who think about and experience physics in the park develop a deeper understanding of the principles taught in the classroom. They demonstrate this understanding by always coming back with original questions. By becoming part of the laboratory equipment, the students experience the excitement of understanding and learning along with the enjoyment of the rides.

We all know how self-conscious teenagers can be; it's one of the scourges of the age. One benefit of the group experience at the park is that because all of the students are doing physics, none of them feels out of place. Working in teams is a realistic reflection of how science is actually done, and the subliminal message is that they can be engaged in an intellectual enterprise, in public, with others, and still remain normal. Getting soaked together on a water-flume ride is a powerful antidote to the elitism which plagues the public image of physics.

This handbook is intended to present all of the information you need both to plan a trip to a park and to use the physics of amusement park rides in your classes. Certain sections are addressed to the teacher. Other sections are ready to be copied and used "as is" by students.

The material in this book has been tested in workshops across the United States and Canada, and suggestions from the workshop participants have helped to shape it. This handbook provides you with everything that you will need to get started. No doubt you will add to the material as you create your own problem sets and park activities.

# Teacher's Guide

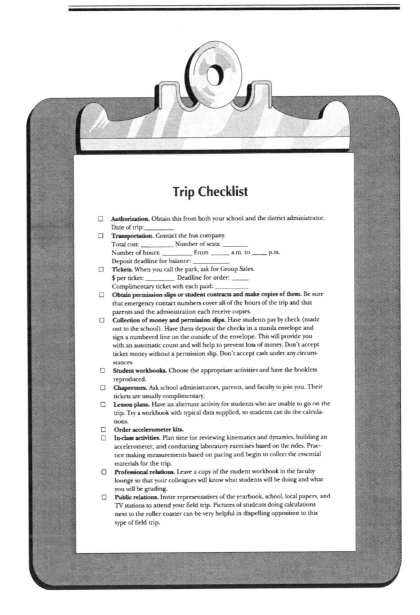

## Trip Checklist

☐ **Authorization.** Obtain this from both your school and the district administrator.
  Date of trip: _____
☐ **Transportation.** Contact the bus company.
  Total cost: _____ Number of seats: _____
  Number of hours: _____ From _____ a.m. to _____ p.m.
  Deposit deadline for balance: _____
☐ **Tickets.** When you call the park, ask for Group Sales.
  $ per ticket: _____ Deadline for order: _____
  Complimentary ticket with each paid: _____
☐ **Obtain permission slips or student contracts and make copies of them.** Be sure
  that emergency contact numbers cover all of the hours of the trip and that
  parents and the administration each receive copies.
☐ **Collection of money and permission slips.** Have students pay by check (made
  out to the school). Have them deposit the checks in a manila envelope and
  sign a numbered line on the outside of the envelope. This will provide you
  with an automatic count and will help to prevent loss of money. Don't accept
  ticket money without a permission slip. Don't accept cash under any circumstances.
☐ **Student workbooks.** Choose the appropriate activities and have the booklets
  reproduced.
☐ **Chaperones.** Ask school administrators, parents, and faculty to join you. Their
  tickets are usually complimentary.
☐ **Lesson plans.** Have an alternate activity for students who are unable to go on the
  trip. Try a workbook with typical data supplied, so students can do the calculations.
☐ **Order accelerometer kits.**
☐ **In-class activities.** Plan time for reviewing kinematics and dynamics, building an
  accelerometer, and conducting laboratory exercises based on the rides. Practice making measurements based on pacing and begin to collect the essential
  materials for the trip.
☐ **Professional relations.** Leave a copy of the student workbook in the faculty
  lounge so that your colleagues will know what students will be doing and what
  you will be grading.
☐ **Public relations.** Invite representatives of the yearbook, school, local papers, and
  TV stations to attend your field trip. Pictures of students doing calculations
  next to the roller coaster can be very helpful in dispelling opposition to this
  type of field trip.

# Introduction

In this section we have gathered two sorts of materials: activities that you may want to conduct in class and information that you will need to know to conduct the field trip smoothly.

The first part of this section contains materials directed at the trip itself, from learning objectives to a trip checklist, as well as pre-trip classroom activities. The second part provides materials to be used in the classroom, whether or not you take your students to a park, starting with sample problems and laboratory exercises. A section on accelerometers is included because many teachers have found this to be a far-from-simple lesson to teach and an accelerometer is a useful device to take to the park. Overhead transparency masters dealing with the accelerometer are included to help you with your classroom presentation.

The rotating-swing-ride model is used by some teachers as a laboratory exercise and by others as a demonstration, so we have included plans for building one.

The section on measurement can be used as a booklet for students, in conjunction with measurement laboratory activities. This section and the problem sets are printed so that you can photocopy them.

In the student section you will find worksheets for many different rides. Allowing time for lunch breaks and waiting on line, we have found that a five-ride packet is a realistic assignment. If you can, have your students label their worksheets with the particular name given to that ride by your park. *Students do not have to ride* to do the student activities. Measurements are all ground based except for accelerometer readings, which can be shared by the bravest. I know from experience, a terrified rider learns no physics!

The laboratory exercises have been tested, many examples of the swing ride model have been built, the measurement booklet has been well used, and the tips and precautions have come from many experienced teachers. Use them with confidence. Remember that this handbook is intended to be a starting point for you. Feel free to adjust, alter, or edit the material to suit your particular needs, as well as to use it "as is."

# Learning Goals and Objectives

## Cognitive Goal

Upon the completion of the activities, the student will have an enhanced understanding of the following laws and concepts of physics:

1) Forces
2) Work
3) Power
4) Friction
5) Kinematics
6) Newton's laws of motion
7) Rotational motion
8) Conservation of energy
9) Conservation of momentum.

The student will:

1) Determine the forces acting on a passenger in circular motion rides and roller coasters
2) Determine the changes in forces as the student moves in a vertical circle on a roller coaster
3) Calculate the work done against friction on roller coasters
4) Estimate the power required to haul a roller coaster train and its passengers up the first hill
5) Apply the method of triangulation to determine the heights of and distances to various structures
6) Measure the linear displacement of a chair on the rotating swing ride as it moves through a complete revolution
7) Calculate the centripetal acceleration of a passenger in circular motion by the use of an accelerometer
8) Apply Newton's laws of motion
9) Apply the rules of kinematics and principles of conservation of energy to determine the velocity and acceleration of an object after falling a given vertical distance
10) Calculate the momenta of objects and quantitatively determine conservation of momentum
11) Measure and record the student's personal responses to experiences during various rides.

# Attitude Goal

Upon completion of the activities, the student will develop a positive attitude toward the physical sciences.

The student will:

1)   Be motivated to study physics by being challenged with significant tasks that allow the student to comprehend personal experiences
2)   Gain an appreciation of the physics involved in the design and engineering of the rides
3)   Gain an appreciation for the safety devices built into the rides and controls.

# Appreciation Goal

Upon completion of the activities, the student will bridge the gap between school, work, and life education by seeing them as interactive rather than as isolated from one another.

The student will:

1)   Gain an appreciation of the applicability of physical principles studied in the classroom to large-scale phenomena
2)   Gain an appreciation of the value of working in teams to accomplish measuring and calculating tasks.

# Pre-Trip Class Activities

1. Review kinematics and dynamics. It is helpful to present the students with workbook pages for preview in class. You can give students typical data and have them perform the calculations.

2. To demonstrate a ride, set up a model of a rotating swing ride or a Hot Wheels track with a vertical loop. Students can take measurements of the angle of the swing chains as a function of the speed of rotation, or of the mass of the passengers. They can practice measuring the time needed for a car to pass through a point on the track by taping two cars together to make a measurable train. Ask from what minimum height the car must fall in order to stay on the track of the vertical loop. This experiment is good for both demonstration and laboratory purposes. It leads naturally to the role of friction in consuming energy which would otherwise be available for increased speed. Students are prepared for the fact that their calculation, using ideal conditions, will differ from the actual velocities that they will measure in the park.

3. Construct accelerometers. If you cut the plastic tubing ahead of time, both horizontal and vertical devices in the PASCO scientific kit can be constructed easily in a single class period. Calibrating the horizontal device takes some explanation and is a good homework assignment. Accelerometer kits come in class sets of 15 (15 vertical and 15 horizontal devices). Order using catalog no. ME9426, from PASCO scientific, 10101 Foothills Blvd., Roseville, CA 95678, 1-800-772-8700.

4. Run one of the triangulation activities as a laboratory exercise. The flagpole in front of the school is a favorite object for measuring heights. Remember that the equations assume that the pole is perpendicular to the baseline. If your pole is on a mound, the activity will not give accurate results.

5. Practice measuring by pacing. Triangulating a horizontal distance can lead into a discussion of how we know the distances to stars and across unbridged rivers.

6. Show a videotape or slides of actual rides to give students some concept of the size and speed of certain rides. Slides can be used to practice estimating heights and angles of elevation of devices such as roller coasters.

7. Emphasize that students do not have to take the rides. Only the accelerometer readings are taken on the rides. All other measurements are taken by an observer on the ground.

8. Post a map of the park if you can. Encourage students to ride the most popular attractions *before* the park becomes crowded. Locate the First Aid station and discuss how students can reach you if necessary. Some teachers have students check in with them during a designated time period.

9. Set up laboratory groups for the park. Students should stay in groups for educational and safety reasons. Announce requirements and options, when the work is due, and how it will be graded.

10. Preview the workbooks in class and then collect them for distribution on the bus.

# Tips To The Teacher

1. Equipment needed in the park:

   a) Stopwatch (at least one per group)
   b) Accelerometers (doubling as sextants for angles of elevation)
   c) Measuring string or knowledge of their pace
   d) Calculator, pen, pencil
   e) Ziploc™ bag for student workbook and equipment (for water rides)
   f) Dry clothes.

2. Hand out tickets as they exit the bus. This speeds entry into the park.

3. Remind students to double-check the restraints on each ride. Be sure that they understand that safety is not a joke.

4. Suggest that students can avoid losing time waiting in line for lunch if they pack their own.

5. Announce the lateness penalty for either boarding the bus at school or leaving the park.

6. If the student workbooks are due as the bus arrives back at school, you will get them on time but they will be more ragged than if they are due the next day. Have each team leave one copy of the workbook on the bus. That's the one that will be submitted for grading.

7. An interesting option is to allow students to design activities for rides that are not covered in the workbook.

8. Be sure that your students know how to identify your bus. Put a sign in the front window or a scarf on the antenna.

9. If you do not have students check in with you during the day, make a habit of being visible, and check the First Aid station every hour or so. Students can leave notes for you there.

10. Be sure you have a minimum of two adults on each bus in case you need someone to stay with an ill student.

# Trip Checklist

☐ **Authorization.** Obtain this from both your school and the district administrator. Date of trip:_____

☐ **Transportation.** Contact the bus company.
Total cost: _____ Number of seats: _____
Number of hours: _____ From _____ a.m. to _____ p.m.
Deposit: $_____ Deadline for balance: _____

☐ **Tickets.** When you call the park, ask for Group Sales.
$ per ticket: _____ Deadline for order: _____
Complimentary ticket with _____ paid.

☐ **Obtain permission slips or student contracts and make copies of them.** Be sure that emergency contact numbers cover all of the hours of the trip and that both parents and the administration each receive copies of the contract.

☐ **Collection of money and permission slips.** Have students pay by check (made out to the school). Have them deposit the checks in a manila envelope and sign a numbered line on the outside of the envelope. This will provide you with an automatic count and will help to prevent loss of money. Don't accept ticket money without a permission slip. Don't accept cash under any circumstances.

☐ **Student workbooks.** Choose the appropriate activities and have the booklets reproduced.

☐ **Chaperones.** Ask school administrators, parents, and faculty to join you. Their tickets are usually complimentary.

☐ **Lesson plans.** Have an alternate activity for students who are unable to go on the trip. Try a workbook for which you supply typical data, so students can do the calculations.

☐ **Order accelerometer kits.**

☐ **In-class activities.** Plan time for reviewing kinematics and dynamics, building an accelerometer, and conducting laboratory exercises based on the rides. Practice making measurements based on pacing and begin to collect the essential materials for the trip.

☐ **Professional relations.** Leave a copy of the student workbook in the faculty lounge so that your colleagues will know what students will be doing and what you will be grading.

☐ **Public relations.** Invite representatives of the yearbook, school, local papers, and TV stations to attend your field trip. Pictures of students doing calculations next to the roller coaster can be very helpful in dispelling opposition to this type of field trip.

# Physics Day Field Trip Student Contract

**Faculty Sponsor:** _____

On _____, students participating in the trip to _____ will leave _____ High School at _____a.m. by bus and return that day at about _____ p.m. The cost of the trip will be $_____, which must be paid by check made out to the high school. This agreement, when signed, informs those concerned that the following stipulations are understood and agreed upon prior to departure.

1. Completion of the physics exercises and write-up is mandatory for each student.
2. Each student is responsible for being on time according to the day's schedule.
3. No student is to engage in any activity that might endanger individual safety or cause property damage.
4. No alcoholic beverages will be brought on the buses or consumed on the trip.
5. No drugs (except those prescribed by a doctor) will be permitted on the trip.
6. Any violation of school district policy will result in appropriate disciplinary action.

This agreement is meant to alleviate any misunderstanding that this trip is not a serious educational activity. Physics Day is an opportunity for students to experience physics principles in a meaningful and enjoyable way.

Your signature below indicates that you have read and understood this agreement and that you would like to participate in this experience. **Please have your parent(s) or guardian(s) read this agreement and sign it. Both signatures are necessary before space on the trip can be reserved for you.**

**Important notes:**

*No student is required to go on the rides in order to earn full credit.* Many of the exercises can be done at ground level.

Please list here any medication currently prescribed for you or that you take routinely and any medical information, such as bee sting allergies, that might be needed by First Aid personnel.

Medication: _____

Other medical information: _____

Student: _____ Signature: _____

Parent/guardian: _____ Signature: _____

Emergency contact #s:     Business: _____ Home: _____

# Safety Precautions

1.  Medical records, including information about current medication, should be part of the permission slip. Be sure to carry the slips with you on the trip.

2.  Be sure that students are aware of the location of the First Aid station. Let them know that they can leave messages for you there. Before the trip, let parents or guardians know that you will check the station for messages periodically.

3.  Form laboratory groups of four to six students.

4.  Shoes or sneakers are a must. Sandals, loose footwear, loose jackets, and long hair are dangerous on some rides. Remind your students that they must observe any posted regulations.

5.  Evaluate your measuring devices for safety before you leave school. Avoid anything with sharp ends. Devices must be lightweight and capable of being tethered to the wrist to avoid loss during a ride.

6.  Remind students to check that seat belts and harnesses are secured. The rides are designed to be safe. Students should double-check for themselves.

7.  The sun can be a problem. Sun block and sun visors are a must on what may be their first full day in the sun this year.

8.  Rememb e r –*No one is forced to ride*. Measurements can be taken from the ground and accelerometer readings can be shared.

# Typical Ride Measurements

## Non-Looping Roller Coaster

Angle of inclination of track down
    from first hill, 50°
Height of first hill above the lowest
    point on the track, 36 m
Height of second hill above the lowest
    point on the track, 29 m
Radius of curvature of the valley
    between first two hills, 30 m
Length of train, 12 m
Mass of an eight-car train, 4500 kg
Time to be pulled up first hill, 42 s
Time for the first descent, 3.8 s
Length of first hill, 69 m

## Water Log Ride

Angle of slide, 45°
Height of slide, 25 m
Mass of empty log, 130 kg
Stopping time, 1.6 s
Stopping distance, 6 m

## Carousel

Radius, 7 m
Period of rotation, 25 s
Period of oscillation of a horse, 9 s

## Looping Roller Coaster

Time during which catapult acts, 4.5 s
Height of starting platform, 20 m
Height of top of the loop, 22 m
Length of train, 11 m

## Rotating Swings

Angle of swing to vertical when hub is
    level, 47°

Angle to which the hub can tilt, 15°
    from horizon
Mass of swing, 30 kg
Rotation rate, 10 rpm
Radius from center of hub to swing at
    rest, 7 m
Length of chains, 4.5 m

## Free Fall

Time to fall vertical segment of
    tower, 2.5 s
Time during which brakes are
    applied, 2.6 s
Total height of tower, 30 m
Free fall length of tower, 20 m
Horizontal braking distance, 26 m
Time for entire ride, 5.2 s

## Rotor

Radius, 2 m
Minimum period of rotation, 1.7 s
Total time of ride, 100 s

## Looping Roller Coaster

Height of first hill, 26 m
Radius of lower loop, 22 m
Radius of top of loop, 8 m
Height of loop, 20 m

## Catapulted Roller Coaster

Height of first hill, 51 m
Height of loop, 41 m
Radius of lower loop, 37 m
Radius of top of loop, 5 m
Length of first down slope, 90 m

# Swing Ride Demonstrator

This easily constructed model can be used as a demonstration or for a laboratory activity.

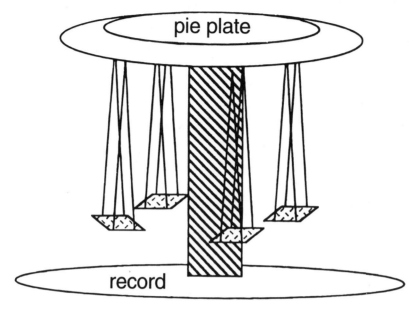

*Swing Ride Demonstrator*

## Materials:

1.  One cardboard tube, wrapping paper roller, roll of school paper towels, or mailing tube 7 to 10 cm in diameter, about 40 cm long
2.  One 23 cm (9 in) metal pie plate
3.  Four strips of corrugated cardboard, roughly 5 cm x 8 cm, to make into seats
4.  Four colored pieces of wool or string about 1.2 m long (at least two colors)
5.  One 30 cm (12 in) phonograph record
6.  Wrapping paper to decorate tube
7.  Scotch™ tape and silicone glue
8.  One phonograph turntable

## Assembly Directions:

1.  Punch four evenly spaced pairs of holes along edge of pie plate.
2.  Invert, center, and glue the plate to the top of the tube.
3.  Center and glue the tube to the phonograph record.
4.  Punch holes close to the corners of the cardboard "seats" or tape string to extra large paper clips.

5.  Thread a piece of string through the holes along the underside of a 5 cm (2-in) edge of a "seat." Make the ends even and thread the pair in and out of a set of holes in the edge of the pie plate. Bring the two ends through the holes on the other edge of the seat and tie them off under the seat as inconspicuously as possible.
6.  Adjust the string so that the seat is level. Repeat for the other three seats.
7.  Decorate the tube as desired. A barber pole effect looks colorful.

**Another option:** Use four extra-large paper clips as seats. Tape the string to the clips and tie off at the perimeter of the plate. Cover with a second plate to hide the knots.

## Tips On Use In Class

- Put coins or miniature dolls on the seats. Apply sufficient weight to put tension on the strings.
- Ask your students which seats will ride at greater angles, the empty ones or those with the most massive rider.
- Place the model on a turntable and run it at 45 rpm. After your students have seen that all seats are at the same angle, ask them whether the speed influences the angle. Now run the turntable at 78 rpm. You will find that the demonstration is much more impressive this time.
- Have your students use either a horizontal accelerometer or a protractor with a weighted string hung from its center to measure the angle of the strings. This is good practice for using the devices in the park.
- Derive the formula for the speed of the swing, given the rpm and the radius of the circle in which the riders travel.
- Have students draw the free body force diagram for a rider. Use it to derive the formula for the angle at a constant speed.
- Try projecting the shadow of the swings onto the board. Draw the strings and measure the angle. This makes it more obvious that all of the swings are at the same angle. Also measure the radius of the circle in which the riders are moving.
- Now you can calculate the centripetal force on one of the riders. If you have a suitable spring, you can even measure the centripetal force by hooking the spring between the central tube and the seat. Hooke's law will give the force it provides because you already know its extension. This also makes it clear that the net force on a rider must be directed inward.
- Compare the actual angle with the predicted angle and the actual centripetal force with the predicted centripetal force.

# Practice Problems

# Kinematics

1.  A roller coaster train which is 12 m long takes 2.3 seconds to pass a certain spot on the track. What is the average speed of the coaster at that point? _____

2.  How fast will an object be moving after falling from rest for 6.0 seconds? _____

3.  How long would it take an object in free fall to drop 75.0 m? _____

4.  A boat starts down a water slide from rest. It takes 14.0 seconds to travel the 40.0 m slide. Assume friction is negligible.

    a.  What was the boat's average velocity? _____

    b.  What was the boat's velocity at the bottom of the slide? _____

5.  The final chute of a log flume is 36 m long. The log starts from rest and takes 4.0 seconds to get to the bottom.
    a.  What is the log's acceleration on the chute that day? _____
    b.  What is the final speed with which the log hits the pool? _____

6.  Assume that the speed with which you enter the stopping track on Free Fall is 28 m/s, and takes you 3.4 seconds to stop.

    a.  What is the stopping acceleration? _____

    b.  What is the stopping distance? _____

7.  The new water ride at the amusement park is called Splash Down. It is different from the Log Flume in that you do not have a zero speed at the top. You can calculate the speed at the top by knowing the length of the boat and how long it takes to come over the hill. A 3 m long boat takes 1.5 seconds to come over the top of the hill at a constant speed. How fast is it going?_____

8.  The elevator of an observation tower ascends 100 m at an average speed of 1.5 m/s. How long does it take the elevator to make one trip to the top? _____

9.  If you did problem #7 correctly, you now know that you come over the top and start down the ramp at 2 m/s. It then takes you 3.2 seconds to get to the bottom of the 50 m long ramp.

    a.  Find the speed at the bottom of the ramp: _____

    b.  After getting soaked, you realize that the boat has slowed down. You time the next boat (which is 3.0 m long) as it goes past a post near the bridge after splash down. It took 2.0 seconds. How slowly did you end up going? _____

   c.    Your laboratory partners noticed that the splash lasted 1.2 seconds. Calculate your stopping acceleration using this time, along with the speeds before and after the splash (the answers from 9a and 9b): _____

   d.    Calculate how far the boat moved while it was slowing down: _____

10.  At the top of the first drop of a roller coaster, a car has a speed of 2.0 m/s. The incline is 50 m long. If it takes 3.8 seconds for the car to travel down the incline:

   a.    Using the distance and time of travel, calculate the average acceleration of the car: _____

   b.    Calculate the final speed at the bottom of the hill: _____

   c.    The first incline makes a 50° angle with the horizon. What is the height of the top of the first hill? _____

11.  The Rotor in an amusement park is a rotating cylinder in which the riders stand against the wall. It takes 1.7 seconds for the drum of the rotor to make one complete revolution. If the average distance of a rider from the center of the drum is 2.0 m and the ride lasts for 100 seconds:

   a.    What is the average speed of a rider? _____

   b.    What is the distance a rider travels? _____

   c.    What is the displacement of a rider from the original position? _____

   d.    If your answers to parts b and c differ from each other, please explain why:

        _____

        _____

        _____

        _____

        _____

# Newton's Laws

1.  A student determines that the first hill of a roller coaster makes an angle of 20° with the horizontal. The hill is 20 m high.

    a.  Find the length of the hill either by trigonometry or scale drawing: _____

    b.  How much force is needed to pull a 50 kg passenger up the hill at a constant speed? _____

2.  Many amusement park rides secure the passengers in seats with high backs and hold them in place with foam-padded harnesses that come over both shoulders and firmly secure the upper body in place.

    a.  What type of ride is most likely to need this type of system to protect the riders?
        _____

    b.  Discuss the reasons for this type of system in terms of the inertia of the passenger and the forces exerted on the passenger:
        _____
        _____
        _____

3.  A 500 kg roller coaster car enters the stopping track at 30 m/s. How much average force is being exerted if the coaster takes 2 seconds to stop? _____

4.  At the beginning of the Free Fall ride at an amusement park, you are released from rest and allowed to fall freely. During the free-fall portion of the ride you do not feel any force between your body and the seat of the car you are riding in (that is, you do feel weightless).

    a.  Draw a vector diagram showing the forces that are acting on your body.

    b.  Explain why you feel weightless:
        _____
        _____
        _____
        _____

5.  The Rotor has a diameter of 6 m and makes 4 rev in 8.4 seconds.

    a.  What is its period of revolution?

    b.  What is the speed of a rider standing against the inside wall?
        _____

    c.  What is the centripetal force on a 50 kg person at the perimeter of the rotator?
        _____

    d.  What is the $\mu$ of the wall if the person does not slide down when the floor drops away? (This means that the force of friction is exactly balancing the force of gravity.) _____

6. Two bumper cars, each having a mass of 100 kg and traveling with a velocity of 1.5 m/s, collide head on. After the collision, both cars have a velocity of 1.0 m/s in directions opposite to their original motion. Find:

   a. The momentum of the first car before the collision: _____

   b. The change in momentum of the second car: _____

   c. The change in momentum of the system: _____

   d. Was this collision elastic or inelastic? _____ Explain:

   _____
   _____
   _____
   _____

7. Bumper cars A and B each have a mass of 100 kg. Bumper car A collides elastically with bumper car B, which is at rest. After the collision, the velocity of car A is 0.8 m/s 30° north of east and car B is 0.6 m/s 60° south of east.

   a. Draw a vector diagram showing the total momentum after the collision.

   b. Find the velocity of car A before the collision: _____

   c. How would the problem change if the collision were inelastic?

   _____

8. A boat hits a splash-down area of the log flume at 12 m/s. The splash, which lasts 0.4 s, results in the boat having a final speed of 3.0 m/s.

   a. What is the momentum of a 52 kg passenger just before the splash?

   _____

   b. What is the momentum of the passenger just after the splash? _____

   c. What impulse did the splash produce? _____

   d. What force did the passenger feel? _____

9. At the beginning of a vertical loop roller coaster, a car with a mass of 1000 kg starts from rest and is accelerated by a constant force to a speed of 35 m/s in 1.4 seconds.

   a. What is the acceleration of the car? _____

   b. What is the magnitude of the force exerted on the car? _____

   c. What is the change in momentum of the car? _____

   d. What impulse is applied to the car? _____

# Swinging and Spinning

1.  A 60 kg child is on the swing ride. Her chair is moving at a speed of 6 m/s in a circle of radius 12 m. Assume an average chain between the two actual chains.

    a.  What is the angle between the chain holding the chair and the horizon?

    _____

    b.  How much force (tension) is the chain exerting? _____

2.  An 80 kg teenager is on the next swing. The chair is moving at the same 6 m/s in a circle of radius 12 m.

    a.  What angle does the chain of the teenager's chair make with the ground?

    _____

    b.  How much force (tension) is the chain exerting?_____

3.  The swing ride speeds up. The chairs are now going at 9 m/s in a circle of radius 15 m.

    a.  Find the chain's angle for a 40 kg child: _____

    b.  Find the force (tension) now exerted by the chain: _____

    c.  What will the chair's angle be for an adult four times as massive (160 kg)? Do you have to calculate? _____

    d.  How much force will the chain need to exert for the adult? Is there a quick way to do this? _____

4.  A 58 kg girl is on a chair on the swing ride. The chairs are moving at 9.1 m/s in a circle of radius 18 m. What angle does the chain make with the ground?

    _____

    (Can't find an answer? Did you use mass...or weight?) (Use 10 m/sec$^2$ for the acceleration due to gravity.)

5.  A Rotor is built with a radius of 3.00 m and the wall has a μ of .5.

    a.  What force is needed to support a 60.0 kg passenger when the floor drops?

    _____

    b.  What normal force must the wall exert to provide the friction force needed?

    _____

    c.  How fast must the rotor be rotating to provide the force calculated in b?

    _____

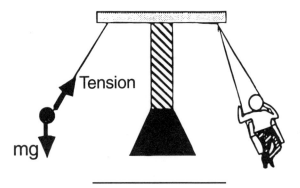

*Figure 1: Swing Ride*

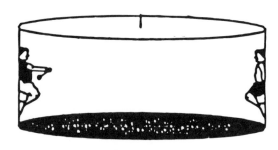

*Figure 2: Rotor*

6. Repeat problem #5 for a 20.0 kg child. How do the answers compare with those in problem #5? Can people of different masses ride safely on the same rotor?

_____

_____

_____

7. How fast must the outer wall of a rotor of radius 1.80 meters be going if it has a µ of 2.0? (Velcro wall!) _____

8. A rotor makes 10 revolutions in 24 seconds. The rotor has a radius of 3 m and the rider in question has a mass of 40 kg.

   a. What is the speed of the rider? _____

   b. What force must friction provide to keep the rider from slipping? _____

   c. What centripetal force is being exerted on the rider's back? _____

   d. Calculate the µ using the above data: _____

   e. Is this the only possible value for the coefficient? Could it be smaller? Could it be larger?

   _____

   _____

   _____

   _____

   _____

# Roller Coasters

1. Shown below is a roller coaster. At points A, B and C find the potential energy, kinetic energy and speed of a passenger whose mass is 60 kg.

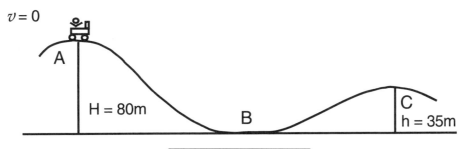

*Figure 1: Roller Coaster*

| A | B | C | |
|---|---|---|---|
| PE = _____ | PE = _____ | PE = _____ | Total = |
| KE = _____ | KE = _____ | KE = _____ | |
| $v$ = _____ | $v$ = _____ | $v$ = _____ | |

2. Using the same roller coaster with a different passenger, find the energies and speeds for a passenger whose mass is 120 kg. Compare with the answers to problem #1.

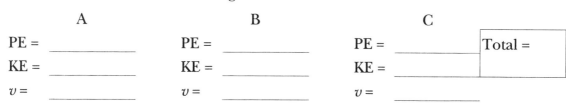

*Figure 2: Roller Coaster with different passenger*

| A | B | C | |
|---|---|---|---|
| PE = _____ | PE = _____ | PE = _____ | Total = |
| KE = _____ | KE = _____ | KE = _____ | |
| $v$ = _____ | $v$ = _____ | $v$ = _____ | |

3.  Let the car start from rest at point A in the looping coaster shown below. Find the potential energy, the kinetic energy and the speed of the rider at points A, B and C. What is the net force (centripetal force) at each point? How much of this force must be provided by the track? Remember that at the bottom of the loop the track must both balance the weight of the car and provide the centripetal force. At the top, the weight helps to provide the centripetal force. The force factor equals the push of the track divided by the weight of the rider. A force factor greater than 4.5 is dangerous. Calculate the force factor at points A, B and C.

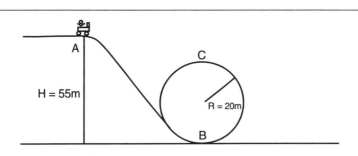

*Figure 3: Catapulted Coaster (circular loop)*

| A | | B | | C | |
|---|---|---|---|---|---|
| PE = | _____ | PE = | _____ | PE = | _____ |
| KE = | _____ | KE = | _____ | KE = | _____ |
| $v$ = | _____ | $v$ = | _____ | $v$ = | _____ |
| $F_{centripetal}$ = | _____ | $F_{centripetal}$ = | _____ | $F_{centripetal}$ = | _____ |
| $F_{track}$ = | _____ | $F_{track}$ = | _____ | $F_{track}$ = | _____ |
| Force factor = | _____ | Force factor = | _____ | Force factor = | _____ |

4.   This looping coaster has a clothoid loop instead of a circular loop. The top of this loop has a smaller radius than the bottom. At points A, B and C, find the potential energy, the kinetic energy, the speed, the centripetal force, the push of the track and the force factor. How does the force factor at the fastest point on the clothoid loop compare with the force factor at the fastest point on the circular loop?

_____

_____

Since the speeds are not very different, the thrill is comparable. Why then do parks only build clothoid loop coasters?

_____

_____

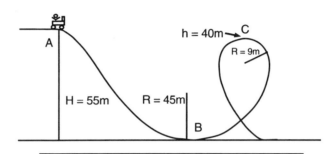

*Figure 4: Catapulted Coaster (clothoid loop)*

|  | A |  | B |  | C |
|---|---|---|---|---|---|
| PE = | _____ | PE = | _____ | PE = | _____ |
| KE = | _____ | KE = | _____ | KE = | _____ |
| $v =$ | _____ | $v =$ | _____ | $v =$ | _____ |
| $F_{centripetal} =$ | _____ | $F_{centripetal} =$ | _____ | $F_{centripetal} =$ | _____ |
| $F_{track} =$ | _____ | $F_{track} =$ | _____ | $F_{track} =$ | _____ |
| Force factor = | _____ | Force factor = | _____ | Force factor = | _____ |

# Answer Keys

## Kinematics

1. $v = 5.2$ m/s

2. $v = at$, $v = 58.8$ m/s

3. $D = \frac{1}{2}\, at^2$
   $t = 3.9$ s

4. Average speed $= \dfrac{\text{distance moved}}{\text{time used}}$
   a. Average speed $= 2.86$ m/s
   b. average speed $= \dfrac{v_i + v_f}{2}$
   since $v_i = 0$,
   final velocity $= 5.72$ m/s

5. a. $D = \frac{1}{2}\, at^2$
   $36$ m $= \frac{1}{2}\, a\, (4\text{ s})^2$
   $a = 4.5$ m/s$^2$
   b. $v_f = v_i + at$
   $V = 18$ m/s

6. a. $v_f = v_i + at$
   $0 = 28$ m/s $+ a\,(3.4$ s$)$
   $a = 8.2$ m/s$^2$
   b. $d = (\text{average speed}) \times \text{time}$
   $d = 14\,\frac{\text{m}}{\text{s}}\,(3.4$ s$) = 47.6$ m $= 48$ m

7. If speed is constant, $v = \dfrac{d}{t}$
   $v = 3$ m/$1.5$ s
   $v = 2$ m/s

8. $v_{avg} = \dfrac{d}{t}$
   $t = \dfrac{d}{v_{avg}}$
   $t = \dfrac{100 \text{ m}}{1.5 \text{ m/s}^2}$
   $t = 67$ s

9. a. Average speed $= \dfrac{d}{t}$
   Average speed $= 50$ m, $3.2$ s $= 15.6$ m/s for constant acceleration

   Average speed $= \dfrac{v_i + v_f}{2}$
   $2(\text{average speed}) - v_i = v_f$
   $v_f = 29$ m/s

   b. $v = 3$ m/$2$ s $= 1.5$ m/s

   c. $a = \dfrac{\Delta v}{\Delta t} = \dfrac{1.5 \text{ m/s} - 29.2 \text{ m/s}}{1.2 \text{ s}}$
   $a = -23$ m/s$^2$

   d. $D = \text{average speed} \times \text{time or}$
   $D = v_i\, t + \frac{1}{2}\, at^2$
   $D = 18.4 = 18$ m

10. a. $D = v_i\, t + \frac{1}{2}\, at^2$
    $50$ m $= (2$ m/s$)(3.8$ s$) + \frac{1}{2}\, a(3.8$ s$)^2$
    $50$ m $- 7.6$ m $= \frac{1}{2}\, a\,(3.8$ s$)^2$
    $a = 42.4$ m $(2)/(3.8$ s$)^2$
    $a = 5.9$ m/s$^2$

    b. $v_f^2 = v_i^2 + 2\, as$
    $v_f^2 = (2$ m/s$)^2 + 2(5.9$ m/s$^2)(50$ m$)$
    $v_f^2 = 4\text{m}^2/\text{s}^2 + 590$ m$^2$/s$^2$
    $v_f = 24$ m/s

    c. Height $= 50$ m $(\sin 50°)$
    $h = 38$ m

11. a. $C = 2\, pr = 12.6$ m
    $v_{avg} = 12.6$ m/$1.7$ s $= 7.4$ m/s

    b. $\dfrac{100 \text{ s (total time)}}{1.7 \text{ s (per rev)}} = 58.8$ rev
    $D$ (total) $= 58.8$ rev $\times 12.6$ m/rev
    $D = 741$ m

c. The ride stops .2 rev short of a complete circle, or 72° away from the start.

Displacement is the straight-line distance from the origin = 2 $r$ sin (72°/2)

Displacement = 2(2 m) sin 36° = 2.35 m left or right, depending on the direction in which the drum rotated.

d. Distance tells how far you actually traveled, or what an odometer would record, without reference to direction. Displacement tells how far and in what direction your final position is from your original position, or how to get to your present position "as the crow flies."

# Newton's Laws

1.  a. Height/Length = 20°, Length = 58.5 m

    b. Work is independent of path therefore $f \times$ Length = $mgh$
    $F$ = 168 N

2.  a. The vertical-loop rides which catapult the riders at the beginning need this type of protection, especially at the point at which the car falls for the first time, because the rider would continue to move forward when the car began to fall. Roller coasters which make sudden sideways moves also need this over-the-shoulder harness.

    b. The harness protects the rider from moving forward suddenly when the car slows or undergoes a

sudden change of direction. Inertia keeps the riders moving in their original direction while the car is changing direction. Without the harness, the only force exerted on the rider, other than weight, is friction between the rider and the seat. This is generally not enough to overcome inertia in the forward-and-back accelerations. In the sideways accelerations, the side of the car would push the riders in the right direction, but they would end up bruised.

3.  $F\Delta t = m\Delta v$     $F$ = 7500 N

4.  a. Vector diagram

    b. Since both you and the seat are falling at the same rate, you cannot press against it. Both are in free fall. We experience weight as the pressure between ourselves and something below us, e.g., the floor or the chair seat. Without that sensation, we feel devoid of weight, i.e., "weightless."

5.  a. $t$ = 2.1 s

    b. $v$ = 9 m/s

    c. $Fc$ = 1350 N

    d. Friction = $mg$ and Friction = $\mu \times$ Normal Force

    The normal force of the wall is providing the centripetal force to keep the person moving in a circle.

$mg = \mu\, Fc$ $\qquad$ $\mu = .36$

6. a. $P_{before} = mv = (100\text{ kg})(1.5\text{ m/s}) = 150\text{ kg m/s}$

b. $P_{after} = mv = (100\text{ kg})(1\text{ m/s}) = 100\text{ kg m/s}$
change in $P = P_{after} - P_{before}$
$\Delta P = 100\text{ kg m/s} - (-150\text{ kg m/s})$
$\Delta P = 250\text{ kg m/s}$

c. Zero. Momentum is conserved in all collisions and explosions in an isolated system. We have assumed friction to be negligible. The bumper cars are therefore isolated from the environment.

d. The kinetic energy of the system before the collision is not equal to the kinetic energy of the system after; therefore the collision is inelastic.

7. a. Vector Diagram:

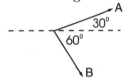

Resultant = 100 kgm/s due east. This is the momentum of car A before the collision.

b. Using the momentum found in step a, the velocity of car A was 1 m/s due east before the collision.

c. If the collision were inelastic, the kinetic energy of the cars after the collision would not equal the initial kinetic energy of car A, but momentum would still be conserved.

8. a. $p_i = mv = 624\text{ kgm/s}$
b. $p_f = 156\text{ kgm/s}$
c. Impulse $= \Delta p = 468$ Ns
d. $J = F\Delta t$
e. $F = 1170$ N

9. a. $a = \Delta v/t = (35\text{ m/s})/1.4\text{ s} = 25\text{ m/s}^2$
b. $F = ma = (1000\text{ kg})(25\text{ m/s}^2) = 25000$ N
c. $\Delta P = [(1000\text{ kg})(35\text{ m/s})] - 0 = 35000\text{ kgm/s}$
d. $Ft = \Delta mv = \Delta P$
Impulse $= 35000\text{ kgm/s}$

# Swinging and Spinning

1. a. $\tan\theta = \dfrac{mgR}{mv^2}$

$\tan\theta = \dfrac{(9.8\text{ m/s}^2)(12\text{ m})}{(6\text{ m/s})^2}$

$\theta = 73°$

b. $T = mg/\sin\theta$
$T = 615$ N

2. a. $\tan\theta = \dfrac{gR}{v^2}$

$\theta = 73°$ independent of mass

b. $T = mg/\sin\theta$
$T = 820$ N

3. a. $\tan\theta = \dfrac{gR}{v^2}$

$\theta = 61°$

b. $T = mg/\sin\theta$
$T = 450$ N

c. 61°, no

d. $T = 4(450\text{ N})$
$T = 1800$ N

4. $\tan \theta = \dfrac{gR}{v^2} = 66°$

5. a. $F_{friction} = mg$
   $F = 600$ N

   b. $F_{friction} = \mu N$
   $N = \dfrac{600 \text{ N}}{.5} = 1200$ N

   c. $N = \dfrac{mv^2}{R}$
   $v = \dfrac{\sqrt{NR}}{m} = \sqrt{\dfrac{(1200 \text{ N}) 3 \text{ m}}{60 \text{ kg}}}$
   $v = 7.8$ m/s

6. a. $F_{friction} = 200$ N
   b. $N = 400$ N
   c. $v = 7.8$ m/s

7. $\mu N = mg$
   $N = mg/\mu$

$v = \dfrac{\sqrt{NR}}{m} = \dfrac{\sqrt{mgR}}{m\mu} = \dfrac{\sqrt{gR}}{\mu}$

$v = \sqrt{\dfrac{(9.8 \text{ m/s}^2)(1.8 \text{ m})}{2}}$

$v = 3$ m/s

8. a. $v = \dfrac{(2\pi R)(10 \text{ rev})}{24 \text{ s}} = \dfrac{(2\pi\, 3m)(10)}{24 \text{ s}}$
   $v = 7.9$ m/s

   b. $F_{friction} = mg$
   $F = 400$ N

   c. $F_c = \dfrac{mv^2}{R}$
   $F_c = 830$ N

   d. $\mu = \dfrac{F_{friction}}{N\, (= F_c)}$
   $\mu = .48$

   e. This is the minimum for this rate of rotation. It could and should be larger.

## Roller Coasters

1. Shown below is a roller coaster. At points A, B, and C, find the potential energy, kinetic energy, and speed of a passenger whose mass is 60 kg.

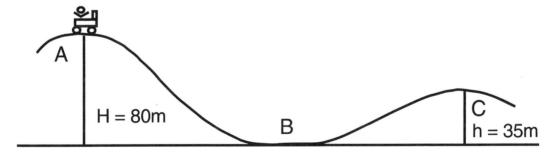

*Figure 5: Roller Coaster*

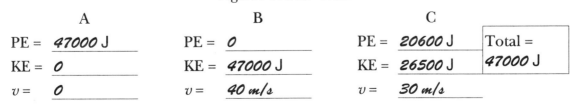

| A | B | C | |
|---|---|---|---|
| PE = *47000* J | PE = *0* | PE = *20600* J | Total = |
| KE = *0* | KE = *47000* J | KE = *26500* J | *47000* J |
| $v$ = *0* | $v$ = *40 m/s* | $v$ = *30 m/s* | |

2. Using the same roller coaster with a different passenger, find the energies and speed for a passenger whose mass is 120 kg. Compare answers to problem # 1.

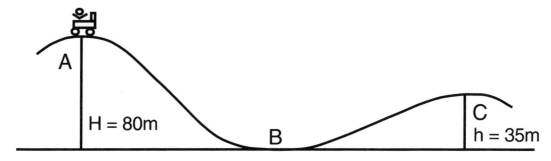

*Figure 6: Roller Coaster with different passenger*

|  | A | B | C |  |
|---|---|---|---|---|
| PE = | **94100** J | PE = **0** | PE = **41200** J | Total = |
| KE = | **0** | KE = **94100** J | KE = **52900** J | **94000** J |
| $v$ = | **0** | $v$ = **40 m/s** | $v$ = **30 m/s** |  |

*Comparison: Speeds are unchanged. Energies are doubled.*

3. Find the energy of, and the forces experienced by, a 50 kg rider in the looping coaster shown below. Remember at the bottom of the loop the track must both balance the weight of the car and provide the centripetal force. At the top, the weight helps to provide some of the centripetal force. Force factor = force of track/weight of rider. A force factor greater than 4.5 is dangerous.

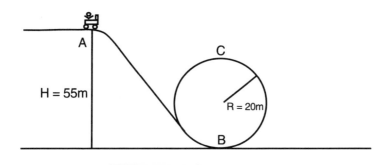

*Figure 7: Catapulted Coaster*

|  | A |  | B |  | C |
|---|---|---|---|---|---|
| PE = | **27000** J | PE = | **0** | PE = | **19600** J |
| KE = | **0** | KE = | **27000** J | KE = | **7350** J |
| $v$ = | **0** | $v$ = | **33 m/s** | $v$ = | **17.2 m/s** |
| $F_{centripetal}$ = | **0** N | $F_{centripetal}$ = | **2700** N | $F_{centripetal}$ = | **735** N |
| $F_{track}$ = | **490** N | $F_{track}$ = | **3200** N | $F_{track}$ = | **245** N |
| Force factor = | **1** | Force factor = | **6.5** | Force factor = | **0.50** |

4. This looping coaster has a clothoid loop instead of the circular loop. The top of the loop has a smaller radius than the bottom.

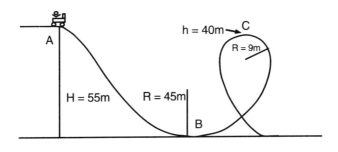

*Figure 8: Roller Coaster with clothoid loop*

| | A | | B | | C |
|---|---|---|---|---|---|
| PE = | 27000 J | PE = | 0 | PE = | 19600 J |
| KE = | 0 | KE = | 27000 J | KE = | 7350 J |
| $v$ = | 0 | $v$ = | 32 m/s | $v$ = | 17 m/s |
| $F_{centripetal}$ = | 0 N | $F_{centripetal}$ = | 1200 N | $F_{centripetal}$ = | 1600 N |
| $F_{track}$ = | 490 N | $F_{track}$ = | 1700 N | $F_{track}$ = | 1100 N |
| Force factor = | 1 | Force factor = | 3.4 | Force factor = | 2.3 |

*The clothoid has a much smaller force factor. Riders are more comfortable and safer in a clothoid loop.*

# Accelerometers

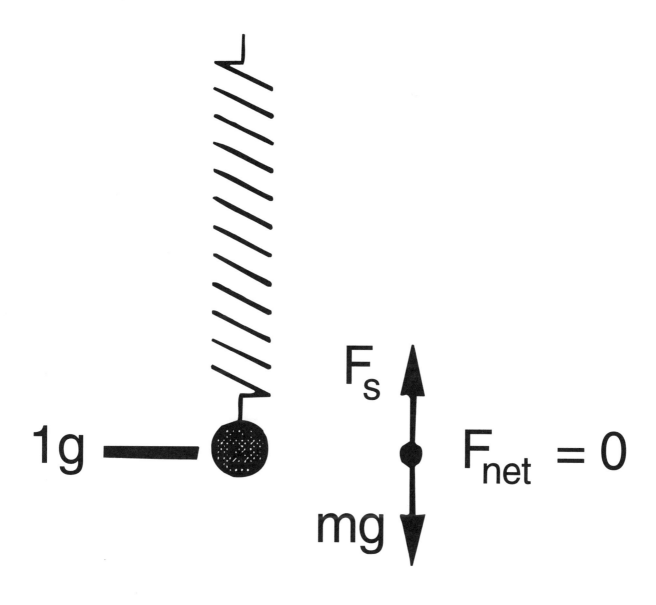

# Types of Accelerometers

## Vertical Accelerometers

Accelerometers are devices that measure acceleration by having something that changes only in response to acceleration. Vertical is used here in the sense of normal to the floor or track of a ride. The vertical accelerometer that we will discuss consists of a lead sinker hung from a spring. It makes use of Hooke's law

$$F_s = -kx$$

where $F_s$ is the restoring force applied by the spring to the sinker and $x$ is the extension or compression of the spring. The negative sign indicates that the force is in the direction opposite to the extension or compression of the spring. As the stretch increases or decreases, the force applied to the sinker increases or decreases in direct proportion. Thus the position of the end of the spring displaced from its equilibrium position indicates the amount of force being applied by the spring.

Calibration of the device can be given in newtons, for the spring force, or, in the ratio

$$F_s/m = \text{an acceleration}$$

because m, the mass of the sinker, remains constant for all uses. With the unstretched spring position taken as the zero point, the weight of a single sinker defines the position corresponding to a restoring force, which has a magnitude equal to the weight of the sinker, or

$$F_s/m = 9.8 \text{ m/s}^2 \text{ or } 1 \text{ g.}$$

Note: If the device is calibrated in units of g, instead of m/s$^2$, it should be pointed out that this unit g is related to the familiar $g$ (local acceleration due to gravity) only in that it has the same magnitude. In class we use the symbol g to mean local gravitational field strength, but here a reading of 2 g on the accelerometer does not mean that the gravitational field has increased. It means that the rider feels a force which is twice the magnitude of the rider's standing-still weight.

### In the reference frame of the rider

It is instructive to analyze the device from the point of view of someone on a ride. The device always registers the acceleration *as seen in the frame of reference of the rider.* Consider the sinker of the accelerometer to be a plumb bob hung from a spring instead of the usual string. The direction response is the same as if it were a plumb bob. The amount by which the spring stretches gives the weight of the bob in the combined gravitational and acceleration fields of the moving rider.

For the person on the ride, up is toward the head and down is toward the feet whether standing or sitting. The rider cannot tell the gravitational field in one direction from an acceleration in the opposite direction. You and I know that the origins of the forces are not the same, but for the sinker, or the person using an accelerometer, the acceleration registered by the device feels like a gravitational field. The readings on the accelerometer correspond to what a rider feels as the local gravitational field.

Because we cannot feel the difference between a gravitational field and an acceleration field, a rotating space station can simulate gravity. The force applied to the rider's feet by the inner surface of a rotating space station would feel just like the normal upward push of the floor. The upward push is normally interpreted as being due to the downward pull of gravity. An equal force, provided by a spinning environment, would feel just like normal gravity. When the wall of a rotating ride pushes in, the person inside feels as though an outward acceleration and force is being applied.

The accelerometer always agrees with what the rider feels because it registers the acceleration in the reference frame of the rider. Upside down, at the top of a vertical circle, such as a roller coaster loop or a rotating ride, the rider may feel little if any force from the seat. The rider feels almost "weightless." At the same point the accelerometer shows little if any pull being applied by the spring. They are in agreement. At the bottom of the same loop, the strong upward push from the seat feels to the rider like a force pushing down into the ground. This upward force is applied to the sinker by the spring, which stretches strongly, giving a large reading. In both cases the rider sees the spring being pulled down toward the rider's seat, which conforms with the downward push the rider feels.

An acceleration smaller than 1 g occurs after the tops of roller coaster hills, when an elevator begins its downward trip, or when one begins to slide downhill. Riders experience a sinking feeling because less force is being applied upward (toward their heads) than that to which they have become accustomed. On some rides, the downward force is partly a push from the safety bar. This downward push feels as if the rider has suddenly become lighter and is rising out of the seat. Sure enough, the accelerometer reads less than 1 g.

All of us have experienced upward accelerations in elevators as they begin to rise. We also experience them at the bottoms of vertical loops on roller coasters and swings. As an elevator begins to rise (accelerates), the floor must push up with a force greater than our weight. We interpret this as an increase in downward force and we feel heavier. The accelerometer spring, stretching to provide the additional force for the sinker, registers more than 1 g. Both the direction and the magnitude of the readings agree with the rider's feeling of an altered gravitational field.

**For an observer on the ground**

In class we usually analyze motion from the point of view of an observer standing on the ground. We ask our students to diagram the forces acting on a body, to find the net force, and then to apply Newton's second law and find the acceleration. In the following exercises, we do this for the sinker in the accelerometer.

When the device is held vertical, the net force on the sinker is given as

$$F_{net} = F_s - W$$

where weight $W$, the weight of the sinker, is expressed in $mg$. If the accelerometer is at rest, the spring force is equal in magnitude to the weight but in the opposite direction. The net force on the sinker is zero, and the acceleration of the sinker is zero. All the spring is doing is supporting the weight of the sinker. This is also true if the device is moving up or down with constant velocity. Because the readings correspond to the spring force, the accelerometer reading is 9.8 m/s$^2$ or 1 g when the net force is zero and the spring is in its neutral position. That is:

$$F_{net} = F_s - mg \qquad \text{Note that this is g, not } g.$$
$$0 = F_s - mg. \qquad \text{The accelerometer reads 1 g.}$$

If the sinker is accelerating upward, the spring must provide enough additional upward force to produce the acceleration. With $F_s$ greater than $W$, the acceleration is greater than zero and upward. In this case, the spring will have stretched downward more than when at rest. When the net force is upward, the device reads greater than 1 g.

$$F_{net} = F_s - mg \qquad \text{positive}$$
$$F_s = F_{net} + mg$$

When the sinker is accelerating downward, the spring must be applying less force than the weight. The spring will have stretched less than when it is at rest. The net force is downward. To find the net acceleration

$$F_{net} = F_s - mg \qquad \text{negative}$$
$$F_s = -F_{net} + mg$$
$$F_s < mg$$

Assume that the sinker is dropping in free fall. Its downward acceleration is 9.8 m/s$^2$.

$$F_{net} = F_s - mg$$
$$F_{net} = -ma \qquad \text{Note: In free fall, } a = g.$$
$$-mg = F_s - mg$$
$$F_s \text{ must} = \text{zero.} \qquad \text{The reading is zero.}$$

Students are often confused by the fact that when falling, the sinker is higher in the tube than the zero g position, and when accelerating upwards, the sinker is lower in the tube than the zero position. It is helpful to have them drop the accelerometer several times in an upright position and watch the spring. They see that during the very brief fall, the spring is not stretched and the sinker therefore is higher in the tube than when it is at rest. With enough experience they will remember in which direction the sinker moves.

Upside down at the top of some looping roller coasters, the spring force is typically some fraction of the weight. As the spring is also upside down, the spring force is now directed toward the ground and so the total vertical force is the weight and the spring force–both downward. The net force on the sinker is now greater than its weight and is accelerating at slightly greater than 9.8 m/s$^2$.

$$F_{net} = -F_s - mg$$

Ascending or descending the loop, the net force on the sinker is the vector addition of its downward weight and the inward pull of the spring. The accelerometer spring reacts only to the force along its axis. Assuming that the device is held perpendicular to the track, the centripetal force can be computed. At the point in the loop where the weight is perpendicular to the direction of the spring, the spring force is just the centripetal force, and the accelerometer reading gives the centripetal acceleration directly.

This is what occurs on a rotor ride, when the accelerometer is held horizontally. The spring does for the sinker what the push of the wall does for the rider. The other forces acting on the rider, the weight downward and the upward friction force, have no components in the horizontal direction, so the accelerometer reading shows the centripetal acceleration less any acceleration due to a horizontal friction force. Line up the accelerometer with the local field to minimize friction.

## Horizontal Accelerometers

Horizontal accelerometers do not share the confusion between feeling and freebody diagrams that occurs with vertical devices. At rest, the metal pellets in the horizontal accelerometer settle to the bottom of the curved plastic tube. The tubing applies a force to the metal pellets in a direction perpendicular to the inner surface of the tube, or along the lines drawn to indicate the angles. When they lie at the bottom, there is no horizontal force applied, therefore there is no horizontal acceleration. The bottom should be calibrated as the zero point.

When the metal pellets are in a stable position above the bottom, the tube force acts along the angle $\theta$, measured from the vertical. It has both a vertical component and a horizontal component directed toward the center of the card. The other force acting on the metal pellets is their weight. If the card is swung in a horizontal circle, the resultant of these two forces is a horizontal force which provides the centripetal acceleration.

The horizontal force equals *ma* and is opposite the angle θ while the weight is adjacent, thus:

$$\tan \theta = ma/mg$$
$$ma = mg \tan \theta$$

Again we calibrate the device to read the horizontal force divided by the mass of the metal pellets:

$$a = g \tan \theta$$

where *a* is the horizontal component of the acceleration and is directed inward toward the center of the device.

To use the horizontal accelerometer, hold it perpendicular to the direction in which the riders are headed and keep it as level as possible. For example, on the rotor ride at an amusement park, where the rider is in a rotating vertical cylinder, hold the accelerometer with the short side pressed to the wall. It will be level with the floor and, since the rider is traveling sideways, it will be perpendicular to the direction of travel.

Before the motion begins, the metal pellets sit in the bottom of the tube. When the ride begins to rotate, a centripetal force is needed to make them go in a circle. The metal pellets will ride up the side nearest the wall, as if forced outward. In fact, the tube will be exerting a horizontal force on them, directed inward toward the center of the ride. They will ride up until the angle is large enough to give the necessary horizontal acceleration. In circular motion, at constant speed:

$$a = v^2/r$$

where v is the linear speed along the circumference and r is the radius of the circle. As the ride picks up speed, a larger acceleration is needed, and the metal pellets will travel further up the curve. Once again the motion of the metal pellets away from the center of the ride agrees with the rider's feeling of being pushed to the wall.

In summation, decide for yourself whether you want your students to look at the motion from the frame of reference of an observer on the ground or from the point of view of the person undergoing the motion. If the vertical accelerometers are calibrated to read zero when at rest, the readings will coincide with what the rider is feeling. But a free body diagram is needed to find the net or resultant force. The overhead transparency masters on the following pages have *rules* that transform the accelerometer reading into a net force for accelerometers calibrated to read 1 g at rest.

# Vertical Accelerometer Physics
## Standing Still or
## Moving at Constant Speed

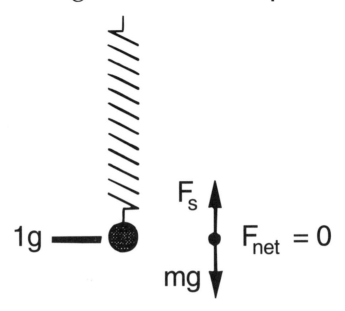

---

**Spring force is equal to weight—
Net force is zero—
Net acceleration is zero.**

---

# RULE:
# If you are "head upward," subtract
# 1 g from the reading on the
# accelerometer.

# Vertical Accelerometer Physics
## Bottom of Roller Coaster Dip
## Bottom of a Loop

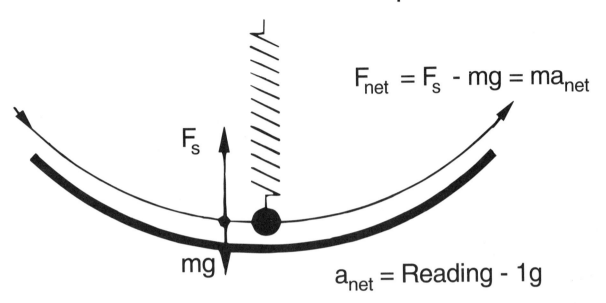

$$F_{net} = F_s - mg = ma_{net}$$

$F_s$

$mg$

$$a_{net} = \text{Reading} - 1g$$

---

**Spring force is larger than object's weight—
Net force is in upward direction—
Net acceleration is in upward direction—
Net acceleration is positive.**

---

# RULE:
# If you are "head upward," subtract 1 g from the reading on the accelerometer.

# Vertical Accelerometer Physics
## Top of a Roller Coaster Bump

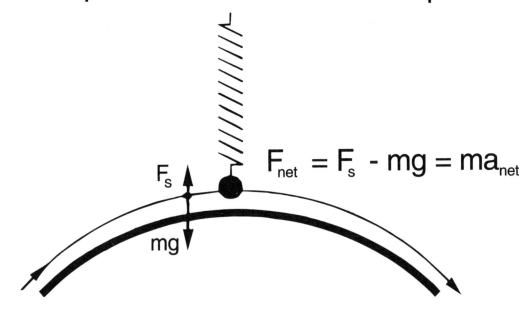

$$F_{net} = F_s - mg = ma_{net}$$

---

**Spring force is less than object's weight—**
**Net force is in downward direction—**
**Net acceleration is downward—**
**Net acceleration is negative.**

---

# RULE:
# If you are "head upward," subtract 1 g from the reading on the accelerometer.

---

# Vertical Accelerometer Physics
## Top of a Vertical Loop
## (Upside Down)

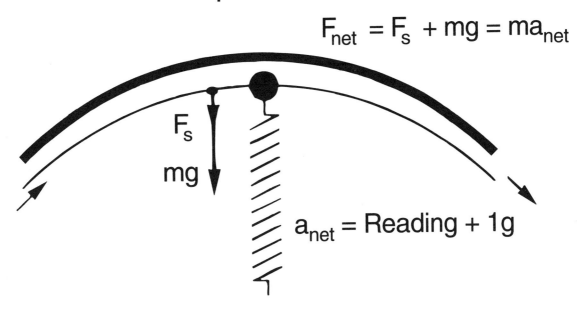

$$F_{net} = F_s + mg = ma_{net}$$

$$a_{net} = \text{Reading} + 1g$$

**Spring force is in same direction as object's weight—
Net force is sum of both forces—
Net acceleration is downward—
Net acceleration is negative.**

# RULE:
# If you are "head downward," add 1 g to your accelerometer reading.

# Vertical Accelerometer Physics
## Circular Ride
## (Accelerometer Sideways)

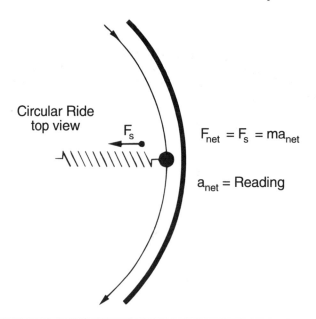

Circular Ride
top view

$F_s$

$F_{net} = F_s = ma_{net}$

$a_{net} = $ Reading

---

**Object's weight is not a factor here—
Net force is in inward direction—
Net acceleration is inward.**

---

# RULE:
# If you are "sideways," just take the reading on the accelerometer.

# Measurement Booklet

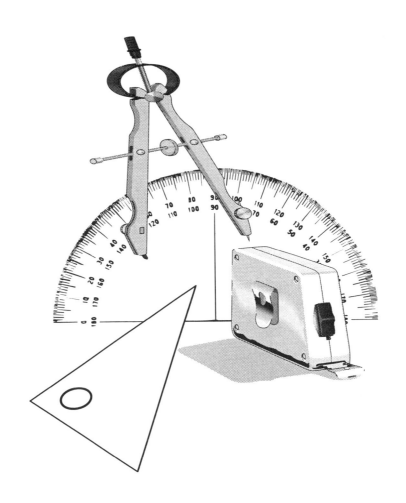

# Suggestions For Making Measurements

## Time

The times that are required in the student activity workbooks can easily be measured using a watch with a sweep-second hand or a digital watch with a stopwatch function. When measuring the period of a ride that rotates or swings, measure the time for several repetitions of the motion. This will give you a better estimate of the period of the motion than a single measurement of one repetition.

When measuring a single event on a ride (for example, the time required for a train to pass a given point), measure the time for several trains to pass the point, then average them.

## Distance

Since you cannot interfere with the normal operation of the rides, you will not be able to directly measure heights or diameters. All but a few of the distances needed in the problems will have to be measured remotely. Following are a few suggestions on how to obtain reasonable estimates of needed distances.

1.  **Pacing:** Determine the length of your stride by walking at your normal rate over a measure distance – for example, the length of a hallway at school. Count the number of steps you take to cover this distance. Knowing the distance and the number of steps taken, you can determine the average distance covered per step. This technique can be used, for example, to determine the circumference of a carousel.

2.  **Ride Structure:** Distance estimates can be made by noting regularities in the structure of the ride. For example, the track on the roller coaster has regularly spaced cross-members. *(See Figure 1.)* The distance *d* can easily be estimated. By counting the number of cross-members, you can determine the distance along the track. Similarly, an estimate of the distance between supporting members can aid in determining horizontal distances. Knowing both horizontal and vertical distances, you can determine the angle of the track. Some students have taken photographs of a structure and, knowing one distance in the photograph, have used scaling

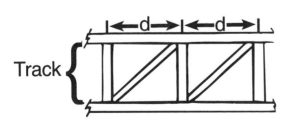

*Figure 1: Roller Coaster track*

techniques to determine other distances along the ride.

3. **Triangulation:** For measuring heights, you can construct a device such as that shown in *Figure 2*. This device can also be used as an accelerometer. The way this device is used is shown in *Figure 3*. Suppose the height *h* of the free fall tower is to be determined. First the distance *L* is estimated by pacing it off or by some other suitable method. Focus on the top of the tower through the soda straw and read the angle θ from the protractor. Note: angle θ is the difference between the position of the straw and the 90° mark on the protractor. It is also the angle of elevation of the soda straw above the horizon. Because

$$h/L = \tan \theta$$

$h$ is given by $h = L \tan \theta$.

Remember to add the distance from the ground to your eye to get the total height.

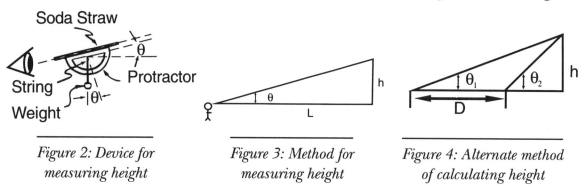

| Figure 2: Device for measuring height | Figure 3: Method for measuring height | Figure 4: Alternate method of calculating height |

If you find it difficult to measure or estimate the length *L*, the following technique can be used. Assume that you need to determine the height *h* in *Figure 3: Method for measuring height*. Standing back at some distance from the tower, measure angle $\theta_1$. Walk directly toward the tower and record the distance D. Measure angle $\theta_2$. Knowing $\theta_1$, $\theta_2$, and D you can calculate the height by using the expression:

$$h = D \ (\sin \theta_1 \sin \theta_2 )/\sin (\theta_1 - \theta_2).$$

# Speed

The average speed of an object is determined by

$$v_{avg} = d/t$$

where *d* is the distance traveled in time *t*. This is straightforward, since *d* and *t* can be measured as discussed above. However, there are two basic types of speed computation involved in the problems, one where speed is fairly constant and another where speed is changing. When the speed is constant for a fairly long time, the speed can be measured. For example, on a rotor ride, the speed of rotation is constant, so if $n$ revolutions occur in time $t$, the speed is given by:

$$v_{avg} = \frac{d}{t} = \frac{n \text{ (circumference)}}{t}$$
$$v_{avg} = n2\pi r / t$$

When the speed is changing and the speed needs to be estimated at a particular point along the ride, the time interval should be as short as possible. This involves determining how far the object moves in this interval. On the roller coaster, the speed at certain points along the track must be found. One simple way to do this is to measure the length of the train and the time required for the entire train to pass the point on the track. The train's average speed at that point is then given by:

$$v_{avg} = \frac{\text{length of train}}{\text{time to pass point}}$$

## Acceleration

### If you are not riding

The acceleration of a person on a ride can be determined by direct calculation. The acceleration calculations required in the problems are of two basic types:

1.  Acceleration down an inclined plane

2.  Centripetal acceleration of an object moving with uniform circular motion

1.  **Inclined planes:** The average acceleration is defined as:

$$a_{avg} = \text{change in velocity/time}$$
$$a_{avg} = \frac{v - v_0}{t}$$

where the subscript $_0$ indicates the initial value. Assume that the acceleration of a train down a hill is to be calculated. First determine $v_0$ by measuring the time it takes for the train to pass over the top of the hill, then find its speed $v$ at the bottom of the hill in the same manner. Since $t$ is the time required for the train to change its speed from $v_0$ to $v$, this is the time elapsed as the train moves from the top to the bottom of the hill. Measure this time and calculate the acceleration using the equation above.

If $v$ at the bottom is not known but the length of the track from the top to the bottom is known, the average or (assumed) constant acceleration can be found by using:

$$d = v_0 t + \tfrac{1}{2} at^2$$

2. **Circular Motion:** Recall that an object undergoing uniform circular motion has a speed given by

$$v = 2\pi r/t$$

where $r$ is the radius of the circle and $t$ is the period of time needed for one complete rotation, and that the centripetal acceleration is given by:

$$a = v^2/r.$$

To calculate the acceleration, measure $r$ and $t$.

3. To measure horizontal accelerations, you might use the device shown in *Figure 5*. An arc of a circle is cut from a sturdy piece of cardboard and a clear plastic tube containing three metal pellets is inserted. Tape the ends of the tube closed, then tape the tube to the cardboard.

As the device is accelerated, the metal pellets will ride up the plastic tube. On a rotating ride, they go up the tube toward the outside of the circle, away from the center. As a roller coaster starts up, the metal pellets travel toward the rear. Both of these motions can be understood if you remember that the tube is the only thing exerting force on the metal pellets (aside from their weight).

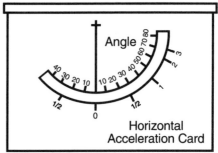

*Figure 5: Horizontal acceleration card*

The cardboard can be labeled directly in gs ahead of time as follows. The push of the tube on the metal pellets has an upward component expressed as $mg$ (the weight of the metal pellets) and an inward component which is the resultant force ($ma$) as shown in *Figure 6: Push of the tube on the pellets*. Because $mg$ and $ma$ are at right angles to one another and the angle $\theta$ is opposite the horizontal component:

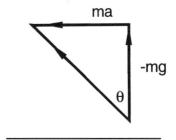

*Figure 6: Push of the tube on the pellets*

$$\tan \theta = ma/mg \text{ or}$$
$$a = g \tan \theta$$

To use the device, hold it horizontal, pointed in the direction of the acceleration, and read the acceleration directly from the position of the middle pellet.

A soda straw taped to the top provides a sighting tube. You can draw protractor readings on the back of the device for use in triangulation.

## If you are riding

1.  A simple device for measuring vertical accelerations is a 0.5 newton spring scale with a 100 g mass attached. When measuring upward accelerations such as those at the bottom of a roller coaster hill, the spring scale is held upright, as shown in *Figure 7*. The forces on the mass are as drawn, where $F_s$ is the reading on the scale. Apply Newton's second law:

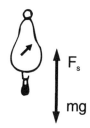

$$F_s - mg = ma$$

The acceleration of the mass is:

*Figure 7: Newton Spring Scale*

$$a = F_s - mg / m$$

2.  A more secure device* is shown in *Figure 8*. The mass and the spring are enclosed in a clear plastic tube, such as a plastic tennis ball can or the clear tube in which laboratory thermometers are shipped. The scale is taped to the tube. Hold it upright and at rest and then mark it zero.

    Add a second mass, and mark the new position 1 g to indicate that when the single mass is at this position the net force is *mg* and it is accelerating upward at 9.8 m/s$^2$. Remove the second mass before using the device in the park.

    Put a mark above zero at the same distance as that for 1 g. When the mass rides at this position it is accelerating downward at 9.8 m/s$^2$.

    At the inside of the top of a loop, the device will be upside down with respect to the ground. The spring should still be exerting some small force and the mass will be at a position closer to the bottom of the tube than the zero position. Whether you call this

*Figure 8*

*This device is available in kit form from PASCO scientific in class sets, catalog no. ME9426, 1-800-772-8700.

a negative acceleration or a positive acceleration depends on your frame of reference. (See the section on accelerometers for a complete discussion.)

An advantage of this design is that it is windproof.

*Be sure to attach the mass to the spring so that it cannot come loose on a ride. Also, tether the device to your wrist with a rubber band or string.*

# Laboratory Exercises

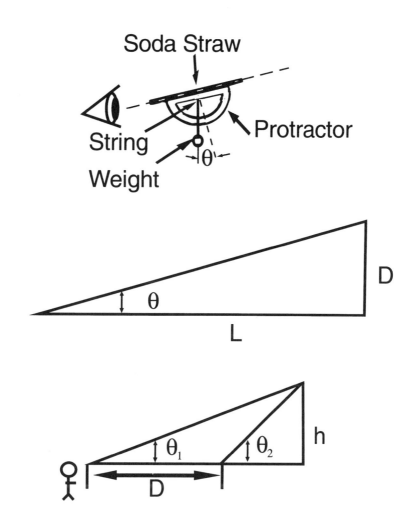

Name: _____ Date: _____ Class: _____

# Elevator Laboratory Exercise

**Purpose:** To investigate accelerations of an elevator.

**Materials:** Vertical accelerometer

**Procedure:**

1.  Without disturbing the normal use of the elevator, ride up and down while holding the accelerometer vertically. Ride part of the time with your eyes closed.
2.  Record the readings when starting an ascent.
3.  Record the readings when stopping an ascent.
4.  Record the readings when starting a descent.
5.  Record the readings when stopping a descent.
6.  Record the accelerometer readings while the elevator is neither starting nor stopping (i.e., riding at a constant speed).

**Data:**

| Accelerometer Readings | 1 | 2 | 3 | 4 |
|---|---|---|---|---|
| Starting an ascent (up) | | | | |
| Stopping an ascent | | | | |
| Starting a descent (down) | | | | |
| Stopping a descent | | | | |
| Riding at constant speed | | | | |

**Questions:**

1.  How is the feeling different when you are accelerating upward from when you are accelerating downward? _____
2.  Can you tell with your eyes closed whether you are accelerating or not? Explain how you can tell. _____
3.  How do the readings for starting accelerations going up compare with those for stopping accelerations going up? _____
4.  How do the readings for starting accelerations going down compare with those for stopping accelerations going down? _____
5.  Sketch an acceleration-time graph for a typical ride up and down. From it, sketch the velocity-time and the displacement-time graphs.
6.  Diagram the forces on a rider accelerating upward. Repeat for downward acceleration.

Name: _____ Date: _____ Class: _____

# Triangulation Laboratory Exercise

**Purpose:**

1.  To measure the height of a flagpole using triangulation.
2.  To measure the distance to a flagpole using triangulation.

**Materials:**

Protractor with plumb bob or horizontal accelerometer
Meter stick

**Procedure:**

Choose a structure such as the flagpole or an edge of the school building. Be sure that you can lay out your baseline on a sidewalk or lawn that is perpendicular to the structure you are measuring. Bring a partner to assist you.

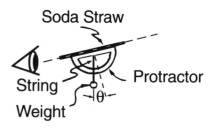

*Figure 1: Protractor with plumb bob*

1.  To measure height:
    a.  Standing about 20 m away, sight the top of the pole. *(See Figure 1.)* Record the angle up from the horizon. This is $\theta_1$ in *Figure 2*.
    b.  Walk directly toward the pole for 5 to 10 m. Measure this distance.
    c.  Sight the top of the flagpole again and record the angle with the horizon. This is $\theta_2$ in *Figure 2*.
    d.  Have your partner measure the distance from your eye to the ground.
    e.  Calculate $h$

$$h = D \times \frac{(\sin \theta_1 \sin \theta_2)}{\sin (\theta_2 - \theta_1)} \text{ plus eye to ground distance.}$$

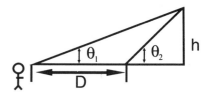

*Figure 2: Measuring height*

2.  To measure distance:
    a.  Pick a point on the flagpole which is about the height of your eye.
    b.  Holding the sighting device *horizontal*, sight this point on the flag pole.

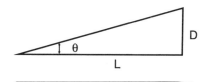

*Figure 3: Measuring distance*

c. Refer to *Figure 3*. Mark this end of your baseline on the sidewalk and then walk directly to your left about 10 m. Have your partner measure the length of the baseline L. Remember that the baseline should be perpendicular to the first sighting line.

d. Holding the sighting device horizontal, sight the point on the flag pole again. Record the angle between the baseline and the sighting line.

e. Calculate *D*.     $D = L \tan \theta$

**Data:**

To find height:

$\theta_1 =$ _____ $\theta_2 =$ _____     Baseline = _____ m  Eye height = _____ m

To find distance:

$\theta =$ _____     Baseline = _____ m

**Results:**

Height = _____ m     _____ % difference from known value

Distance = _____ m     _____ % difference from known value

**Questions:**

1. How do the results of different laboratory groups compare?

_____
_____
_____
_____

2. Estimate the plus or minus (+/-) margin of error in each of your measurements. Do the differences between your group and others fall within your margin of error?

_____
_____
_____
_____

3. What are some of the sources of uncertainty in this exercise?

_____
_____
_____

# Student Workbook

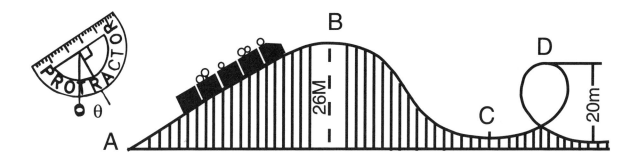

# Introduction

Except for the cover page, which needs to have the school name, year, and park name inserted, this section is ready for photocopying. Each ride has a diagram, a section for measurements to be taken at the park, and, on the first page, questions about how it felt or where the forces are great or small. This first page works well for junior high students and non-mathematical classes. The second and subsequent pages are quantitative, with formulas supplied in the left column so that you can cover them if you do not want to include them in your student workbooks.

We introduce in these pages what we have called a force factor. It is the ratio of the applied force to the student's weight. In other places you will see this quantity called "g force," a term which confuses the acceleration due to gravity with force. It is neither "g" nor a force, but rather, a pure, dimensionless ratio. Engineers and other professionals know this, but beginning students of physics have enough trouble distinguishing acceleration from force, so we have avoided the incorrect, though more common, term.

The concept, however, is useful. What all riders experience at the same point on a ride is a force which is this multiple of their weight. Small children and their parents can ride the Rotor simultaneously and safely because they experience different strength forces while they each measure the same force factor of 2 or 3.[1]

Don't expect your students to complete all of the work in this packet. We have found that waiting time cuts deeply into even a full day's trip. Five rides is a reasonable assignment. Working in groups is a good idea both for safety and because students find it enormously instructive. Try to design a booklet which covers as wide a range of concepts as possible in your park.

The parks vie for the biggest and fastest rides, and they give unique names to them. You will need to identify the rides by the names that your park uses. This is especially true of the roller coasters. White out the dimensions on the drawings if you have students measure these distances.

One last tip. Have your stronger students write similar pages for rides not currently covered. They will enjoy the challenge.

---

1    Because everyone feels the same force factor, you can use these answers to grade student work quickly.

**High School**

_____

**Physics Day 199__**

**at**

_____

**Park**

**Team Members:**

_____

_____

_____

_____

_____

**Teacher:** _____

**Rides Studied:**

_____

_____

_____

_____

_____

_____

**Grade:**

_____

_____

_____

_____

_____

_____

# Conscious Commuting

## Exercises to do on the bus

As you ride to the amusement park, be conscious of some of the physics along the way.

### A. Starting up

*Things to measure:*

As the bus pulls away from a toll booth, find the time that it takes to go from rest to 20 miles per hour. You will have to place someone up front to help.

$t =$ _____

*Things to calculate:*
*(Always show equations used and substitutions made.)*

1. Convert 20 miles per hour to meters per second.
   (1 mph = 0.44 m/s)

   $v =$ _____

2. Determine the acceleration of the bus.

   $a =$ _____

3. Using your mass in kilograms and Newton's Second Law, find the average forward force on you as the bus accelerates from rest.

   $F =$ _____

4. Is this force greater or less than the force gravity exerts on you (your weight)?

   _____

5. Calculate the force factor that you felt, using the force calculated in question 3:

   $$\text{Force factor} = \frac{\text{force felt}}{\text{weight}} \quad \text{(The force factor has no unit.)}$$

*Things to notice as you ride:*

1. As you start up, in which direction are you being forced (forward or backward)? _____

2. If someone were watching from the side of the road, what would that person see happening to you in relation to the bus?

   _____

3.  How can you explain the difference between what you experience as the bus starts up and what the observer sees? (You may want to use the idea of frames of reference.) _____

**B. Going at a constant speed.** *Things to do on the bus.*

1.  Describe the sensation of going at a constant speed. Do you feel as if you are moving? _____

2.  Are there any forces acting on you in the direction that you are moving? Explain what is happening in terms of the principle of inertia. _____

**C. Rounding curves**

1.  If your eyes are closed:

    a.  How can you tell when the bus is going around a curve?
        _____

    b.  What do you feel when you are seated facing forward?
        _____

    c.  What do you feel when you are seated with your back against the side of the bus?
        _____

2.  Before the bus starts around a curve, concentrate on a tree or a building that is directly in front of you. From the law of inertia, you know that your body should continue straight ahead unless an unbalanced force acts on it. See if you can answer the following questions:

    a.  What is the direction of the force? _____

    b.  If the turn were tighter (smaller radius), how would the force be different?
        _____

    c.  How is this force applied to your body through (a) the friction of the seat, (b) your seat mate, (c) the wall, (d) the arm of the seat, or (e) a combination of these? Explain.
        _____
        _____

3.  Many of the rides in the amusement park involve going around curves. Be prepared to compare what you are feeling on the bus with sensations on the rides. Predict some differences that you would expect to feel.
    _____
    _____
    _____
    _____

# Roller Coaster

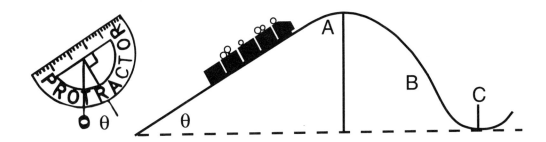

## Measurements

Your mass = _____ kg    Time for first car to reach top of first hill = _____ s
Angle of rise, first hill, θ = ____° Time for first car to travel down first incline = _____ s

**Sensations (normal, heavier, lighter):**    **Meter readings:**

At A, just before descending _____    Force meter = _____
At B, about half way down _____    Force meter = _____
At C, bottom of the curve _____    Force meter = _____

## Observations

1.  What is the advantage of a long, shallow first incline?

    _____

2.  Why is the first hill always the highest?

    _____

3.  Why is the track of the roller coaster banked?

    _____

4.  Where does your meter read closest to zero? _____
    How do you feel at this point?

    _____

5.  What does the near-zero reading tell you about the shape of the track at that
    point?

    _____

6.  Where does the meter give a maximum reading? _____
    Why is it a maximum here?

    _____

# Roller Coaster

## Calculations (Show all substitutions)

$E_p = mgh$

Power = $\dfrac{\text{work}}{\text{time}}$

$F = mg \sin \theta$
work = $mgh$
$F \cdot l$ = work

Force factor = $\dfrac{\text{force felt}}{\text{weight}}$

$v_{average} = \dfrac{\text{distance}}{\text{time}}$

$v_{final} = 2(v_{average})$

$E_k = \frac{1}{2} mv^2$

1. What is your potential energy at the top of the first hill? — Potential energy at top = _____

2. What power is used to get you up the first hill? — Power = _____

3. What is the length of the first hill? — Length = _____

4. What force is used to get you up the first hill? — Force = _____

5. How many times your normal weight is this? — Force factor = _____

6. Calculate the average speed from A to C. — Average speed = _____

7. What is your speed at the bottom of the first hill, based on the average speed from A to C? — Final speed = _____

8. What kinetic energy does this speed give at the bottom of the first hill? — Kinetic energy at bottom = _____

9. Within experimental error, was your energy conserved? Explain your answer. _____

## Finding the force factor at the bottom of the first drop (Show all substitutions)

At the bottom of the first drop, the track makes an almost-circular arc, as if it were part of a circle of radius 30 m. Use the steps given below to find the force factor that you experience as you go through the low point on the track.

$\Delta E_p = \Delta E_k$
$E_k = \frac{1}{2} mv^2$

$F = \dfrac{mv^2}{R} + mg$

Force factor = $\dfrac{\text{force applied}}{\text{weight}}$

1. Assuming no friction, find the maximum speed at the bottom of the first drop. — Speed = _____

2. In order to go through this curve, the track must exert enough force to both hold you in a circle and balance your weight. Calculate the force that the track exerts on you at the bottom of the loop. — Force$_{applied}$ = _____

3. Calculate the force factor at the bottom of the first valley. — Force factor = _____

4. How did the force factor that you calculated compare with the meter reading at C?

# Looping Coaster

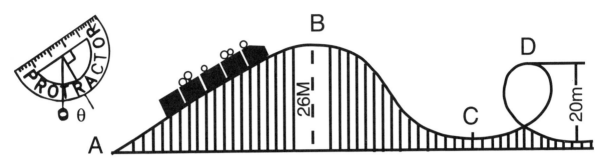

## Measurements

Your mass = _____ kg      Time for first car to reach top of first hill = ____ s
Angle of rise, first hill θ = ____°      Time for first car to travel down from B to C = ____ s

**Sensations (Normal, Heavier, Lighter):**      **Meter Readings:**

At B, just before descending _____      force meter = _____
At about halfway down _____      force meter = _____
At C, bottom of the curve _____      force meter = _____
At D, top of the loop _____      force meter = _____

## Observations

1. What is the advantage of a long, shallow first incline?

2. Why is the first hill always the highest?

3. Why is the track of the roller coaster banked?

4. Where does your meter read closest to zero?

5. How do you feel at this point?

6. What does the near zero reading tell you about the track at that point?

7. Where does the meter give a maximum reading? _____
Why is it a maximum here?

# Looping Coaster

## Calculations (Show all substitutions)

$E_p = mgh$

1. What is your potential energy at the top of the first hill?

Potential energy = _____

$\text{Power} = \dfrac{\text{work}}{\text{time}}$

2. What power is used to get you up the first hill?

Power = _____

3. What is the length of the first hill?

Length = _____

$F = mg \sin \theta$ **or**
work = $mgh$
$F \cdot l$ = work

4. What force is used to get you up the first hill?

Force = _____

$\text{Force factor} = \dfrac{\text{force felt}}{\text{weight}}$

5. How many times your normal weight is this?

Force factor = _____

$v_{average} = \dfrac{\text{distance}}{\text{time}}$

6. Calculate the average speed from A to C.

Average speed = _____

$v_{final} = 2(v_{average})$

7. What is your speed at the bottom of the first hill based on the average speed from A to C?

Final speed = _____

$E_k = \frac{1}{2} mv^2$

8. What kinetic energy does this speed give at the bottom of the first hill?

Kinetic energy = _____

$E_p = mgh$

9. What was your potential energy at the bottom of the first hill?

Potential energy = _____

10. Compare the change in potential energy to the gain in kinetic energy. Within experimental error, was energy conserved? Explain your answer.

_____

_____

_____

_____

_____

_____

_____

_____

_____

_____

_____

_____

_____

_____

_____

_____

_____

# Looping Coaster

## Looping the Loop

$\Delta E_p = \Delta E_k$

$E_k = \frac{1}{2} mv^2$

$F_{bottom} = \frac{mv^2}{r} + mg$

Force factor = $\frac{\text{force felt}}{\text{weight}}$

$E_p = mgh$

$E_k = E_{total} - E_p$

$E_k = \frac{1}{2} mv^2$

$F_{track} + mg = \frac{mv^2}{r}$

Force factor = $\frac{\text{track force (force felt)}}{\text{normal weight}}$

11. If there had been no friction, what would be the maximum speed at the bottom of the first drop?

Speed = _____

12. Going through the curve, the track must exert enough force to both hold you in a circle and counteract gravity. Calculate the force on you at the bottom of the loop.

Force$_{bottom}$ = _____

13. Calculate the force factor at the bottom of the first drop.

Force factor = _____

14. Why is it important that the radius be large at point C?

15. Calculate your potential energy at the top of the loop. (Point D)

Potential energy = _____

16. Assuming conservation of energy, calculate your kinetic energy at the top of the loop.

Kinetic energy = _____

17. What is your speed at the top of the loop?

Velocity$_{top}$ = _____

18. At the top of the loop, gravity works with the track to hold you in a circle. Calculate the force the track exerts on you.

Force$_{track}$ = _____

19. Why is it important that the top radius be small? _____

20. What should the force meter read at the top?

Force factor = _____

21. In the space to the right, draw a diagram showing the forces acting on you when you and the force meter are upside down at the top of the loop, and the meter reads zero.

# Catapulted Coaster

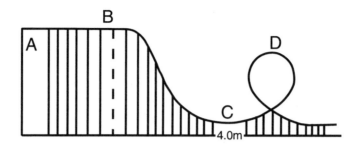

## Observations

1.  Describe what happens between positions A and B and tell how it felt:

    _____

2.  Explain why this portion of the ride is necessary for safety. Think about what would happen at point D if this portion did not exist:

    _____

**Position B**

3.  If you were frightened, it was most likely at point B. Describe how you felt:

    _____

4.  On what part(s) of your body did you feel the largest force?

    _____

5.  Describe what would happen at point B if there were no harness:

    _____

6.  Since the cars are all attached, which car will be fastest at B, first or last?

    _____

**Position C**

7.  Did you feel heavier or lighter than normal at point C? _____
8.  Estimate the force factor for point C: _____
9.  At position C, what parts of your body felt the most force? _____

**Position D**

10. Did you feel right side up or upside down at D? _____
11. Explain the body clues you used. What forces were felt and where? Did you feel as if the harness was holding you in?

    _____

12. How did your reactions differ going backwards from going forward?

    _____

13. Can you tell when you are on the sides of the loop? _____ How? _____

# Catapulted Coaster

## Calculations (show all substitutions)

$E_k = \frac{1}{2}\, mv^2$

1. Your speed at point B is about 10 m/s. What is your kinetic energy at point B?

Kinetic energy = _____

$F \cdot l = work$

2. The catapult pushes the train 20 meters. Calculate the average force exerted on you by the catapult.

Force = _____

$E_p = mgh$

3. Calculate your potential energy at point B.

Potential energy = _____

$E_T = E_p + E_k$
$E_T = \frac{1}{2}\, mv^2$

4. What is your total energy at point B?

Total energy = _____

5. If there had been no friction, what would be the maximum speed at the bottom of the first drop?

Speed = _____

$F_{bottom} = \dfrac{mv^2}{r} + mg$

6. Going through the curve, at the bottom, the track must exert enough force to both hold you in a circle and to balance your weight. Calculate the force on you at the bottom of the loop.

$Force_{bottom} = $ _____

Force factor = $\dfrac{\text{force felt}}{\text{weight}}$

7. Calculate the force factor at the bottom of the first drop.

Force factor = _____

8. Why is it important that the radius be large at point C?

_____

$E_p = mgh$

9. Calculate your potential energy at the top of the loop. (Point D)

Potential energy = _____

$E_k = E_{total} - E_p$

10. Assuming conservation of energy, calculate your kinetic energy at the top of the loop.

Kinetic energy = _____

$E_k = \frac{1}{2}\, mv^2$

11. What is your speed at the top of the loop?

$Velocity_{top} = $ _____

$F_{track} + mg = \dfrac{mv^2}{r}$

12. At the top of the loop, gravity works with the track to hold you in a circle. Calculate the force that the track exerts on you.

$Force_{track} = $ _____

13. Why is it important that the top radius be small?

_____

Force factor = $\dfrac{\text{track force (force felt )}}{\text{normal weight}}$

14. What should the force meter read at the top?

Force factor = _____

# Rotor

## Measurements

Your mass = _____
Time for ten revolutions = _____
Period = _____
Radius = _____
Force meter reading at top speed = _____
(Hold tube horizontal, next to your eyes)

## Observations

1.  Describe how the wall feels and explain why it was constructed this way.

    _____
    _____
    _____

2.  Describe how the force against your back changes as the speed increases.

    _____
    _____
    _____

3.  Have someone on the ride hold an object hanging from a string. Sketch the angle that the string makes with the vertical and describe how the angle changes as the Rotor increases in speed.

    _____
    _____
    _____

4.  Imagine a person throwing a ball at someone directly opposite on the ride. Describe the path the ball would follow:

    a.  As seen by other riders.

        _____
        _____

    b.  As seen by an observer above the ride.

        _____
        _____

# Rotor

## Calculations

$$v = \frac{2\pi r}{T}$$

$$F_c = \frac{mv^2}{r}$$

1. Calculate the maximum speed.

   $v_{max} =$ _____

2. Calculate the centripetal force. (Force exerted by the wall on your back at top speed.)

   Centripetal force =

   _____

3. While you are spinning, three forces are acting on you: gravity, friction, and the push of the wall. Show the forces on the figure.

$$F_{friction} = mg$$

4. Since you do not slide down the wall at top speed, how great is the frictional force? (What is it balancing?)

   Force of friction = _____

$$F_{friction} = \mu F_c$$

5. Compute the minimum coefficient of friction necessary for this ride to operate safely.

   Coefficient of friction

   $\mu =$ _____

Force factor =
$$\frac{\text{force felt (centripetal)}}{\text{weight}}$$

6. Use the centripetal force that you calculated to find the force factor. Compare it with the reading on the force meter.

   Force factor = _____

# Enterprise Rotator

## Measurements

Your mass: _____     Your weight: _____
Time for 4 rotations at top speed (vertical):
time = _____
Period at top speed: $T$ = _____
Radius of rider's seat at top speed: $r$ = _____
Force factor at the bottom = _____
Force factor at the top =     _____

## Observations

1.  Watch the ride as it starts up and sketch what happens to the angle of the cars.
       Stationary          Slow          Just before lift

2.  Describe the sensations the riders experience as the ride accelerates. When do the riders no longer sense the angle of the car?
    _____

3.  Use vector concepts to explain, in terms of forces, why the angle of the car changes as the speed increases:
    _____
    _____

4.  When the ride is vertical

    a.  Where do riders feel the heaviest?

    b.  Where do riders feel the lightest?

    c.  Do riders ever feel upside down? _____

    d.  Describe the rider's sensations when their car is halfway up or halfway down the vertical circle:
        _____
        _____

# Enterprise Rotator

## Calculations (Show all substitutions)

$$v = \frac{2\pi r}{T}$$

1. Calculate the top speed of the car.  Speed = _____

$$F_c = \frac{mv^2}{r}$$

2. Find the centripetal force on you at top speed.  Centripetal force = _____

$$F_{bottom} = F_c + mg$$

3. For the ride in the vertical position, find the force that the seat exerts on you at the bottom of the cycle.  Force$_{bottom}$ = _____

Force factor =
$$\frac{\text{force applied}}{\text{weight}}$$

4. Calculate the force factor that a rider experiences at the bottom of the ride.

Force factor = _____

$$F_{top} = F_c - mg$$

5. For the vertical position, find the force that the seat exerts on you when the car is at the top of the ride (pushing you in toward the center).  Force$_{top}$ = _____

6. Calculate the force factor a rider experiences at the top.

Force factor at top = _____

7. When you are stationary, a seat exerts a force on you that's equal to your weight. You experience a force factor of 1. Based on the force factor when you are at the top of the ride, explain why riders do not feel upside down:

_____
_____
_____
_____
_____

8. How do the calculated values of the force factors (top and bottom) compare to the values measured by the riders?

_____
_____
_____
_____
_____

# Carousel

## Measurements

Period: _____
Number of horses in outer ring: _____
Space between horses: _____
Number of horses in inner ring: _____
Space between horses: _____
Hold the horizontal meter perpendicular
to the horse at top speed and record the angle
with the vertical:
Inner horse: _____
Outer horse: _____

Hold the force meter upright and record the meter readings as the horse goes up and down.
At bottom going up: _____ In middle going up: _____ Arriving at top: _____
At top starting down: _____ In middle going down: ____ Arriving at bottom: _____

## Observations

1.  Is the floor level? _____ If not, which way does it tilt? _____
    Why? _____
    _____

2.  How does the angular velocity of the outer horse compare with that of the inner
    horse? (Compare their revolution rates.)
    _____
    _____

3.  Which horses appear to have the greatest linear speed, the inner or the outer?
    _____

4.  How do the readings on the vertical force meter relate to the force sensations
    that you experienced?
    _____
    _____

5.  How does the radial force meter reading on an inner horse compare with that
    on an outer horse?
    _____

# Carousel

## Calculations (Show all substitutions)

$C = 2\pi r$

$v = \dfrac{\text{Circumference}}{T}$

1. Calculate the circumference of the outer ring (distance between horses times number of horses)

   Circumference = _____

2. What is the radius of this ring?

   Radius = _____

3. Calculate the average maximum speed of an outer horse.

   Maximum speed = _____

4. Calculate the circumference of the inner ring and its radius.

   Circumference = _____

   Radius = _____

5. What is the maximum average speed of an inner horse?

   Maximum Speed = _____

6. How do your calculations compare to the answer to observation #3? Explain.

   _____
   _____
   _____

$F_c = \dfrac{mv^2}{R}$

$F_g = mg$

7. Calculate the centripetal force acting on you when you ride on outer horses.

   Centripetal Force = _____

8. Give your weight in newtons.

   Weight = _____

9. In the space to the right diagram the forces on a rider. Show the angle ß between the vertical and force applied by the plastic tubing. The centripetal force is the resultant force.

$F_c = \dfrac{mv^2}{R}$

10. Compute the centripetal force on you as you ride an inner horse.

    Centripetal force = _____

11. Using your vector drawing, discuss what you expect to happen to ß as you change from an inner to an outer horse. How do your measurements of ß compare with your expectation?

    _____
    _____
    _____
    _____
    _____

# Rotating Swings

## Measurements

Time 2 revolutions at top speed
$t =$ ____
Period = ____
Radius of ride at top speed = ____
Maximum angle chain makes
with the vertical ß = _____
Force meter reading along the chains
at top speed = _____

## Observations

1.  Sketch what happens to the swing as the ride gains speed:

    Start                Slow                Fast

2.  How do you feel as the ride gains speed?

    _____
    _____
    _____
    _____

3.  Compare the angle of the chain with respect to the vertical on an empty swing
    with that of an occupied one at the same radius:

    More                Less                The Same

4.  Describe the change in the motion that occurs as the ride gains full speed:

    _____

5.  Describe the path of the top of the ride:

    _____

6.  How does the force meter reading relate to how you feel on the ride?

    _____
    _____

# Rotating Swings

## Calculations (Show all substitutions)

$$\text{Speed} = \frac{2\pi r}{T}$$

$$F_c = \frac{mv^2}{r}$$

$$F_g = mg$$

1. Calculate the maximum speed of the swings.

Speed = _____

2. Calculate the centripetal force acting on you.

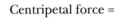
Centripetal force = 

_____

3. If you have not already done so, calculate your weight in newtons.

Weight = _____

4. Sketch all the forces acting on this rider.

5. To find the tension in the chains:
   (1) Draw to scale a horizontal vector representing the centripetal force pointed left.
   (2) Add to it a vertical vector equal in magnitude to your weight but directed upwards. These are the components of the tension.
   (3) Draw the resultant force vector (tension) and determine its magnitude using your scale.

Calculated tension=

_____

Diagram ß = ____°

6. How does angle ß in your drawing compare with angle measured while observing the ride?

_____
_____
_____
_____

7. Multiply the force meter reading by your weight. This gives the measured tension.

Measured tension = ____

8. How does the calculated tension compare with the measured tension?

_____
_____
_____
_____
_____

# Resources

# Selected References

## Journal Articles

Cartmell, Robert, "Roller Coaster, King of the Park," *Smithsonian* 8 (5), 44-49 (1977).

Eckow, Dennis, "Disney World, 15 Years of Magic," *Popular Mechanics*, 67-70 (Nov. 1986).

Escobar, Carole, "Amusement Park Physics," *Phys. Teach.* 28 (7), 446-454 (1990).

*Exploratorium Quarterly,* 11 (1), entire issue (Summer 1987).

Kuczma, Philip A., "Physics of an Amusement Park," *The Science Teacher*, 20-24 (May 1977).

McGehee, John, "Physics Students' Day at Six Flags/Magic Mountain," *Phys. Teach.* 26 (1), 12-17 (1988).

Natale, Kim, "Final Exam in an Amusement Park," *Phys. Teach.* 23 (4), 228 (1985).

Nelson, Robin, "Terror on Wheels, by Design," *Popular Mechanics* 154, 70-73 (Aug. 1980).

Plimpton, George, "American Thrills," *Popular Mechanics*, 39-46 (May 1989).

Roeder, John L., "Physics and the Amusement Park," *Phys. Teach.* 13 (6), 327-332 (1975).

Smith, Marguerite, "Mystery Trains," *MONEY* 18 (8), 53-61 (1989).

Summers, Carolyn, Terry Contnt, and Gódrej Sethna, "Ride-on Physics," *The Science Teacher*, 36-40 (Oct. 1984).

Taylor, George, Joseph Page, Murray Bently, and Diana Lossner, "A Physics Laboratory at Six Flags Over Georgia," *Phys. Teach.* 22 (6), 361-367 (1984).

Walker, Jearl, "The Amateur Scientist," *Sci. Am.* 249 (4), 162-169 (1983).

Walker, Jearl, "Roll 'em," *Science World* 45 (15), 17-19 (1989).

Wolff, Barbara, "Studying Physics on a Roller Coaster," *1990 Science Year, The World Book Annual Science Supplement*, 300-301 (1989).

Also see *Smithsonian Magazine* (August 1989).

## Video

*Perceptual Physics at Cedar Point,* Robert Speers, Bowling Green State Universit y –Firelands College, Huron, OH 44839.

*The Science Connection, Amusing Physics,* Joseph DePuglio, Steinert High School, Trenton, NJ.

Videos of Great Adventure Rides, Laboratory Exercises, and Problem Sets. Available for $29.95 from Thomas Ebeling, Dept. of Curriculum and Instruction, Hamilton Township Public Schools, Hamilton Square, NJ 08690. Make checks payable to Hamilton Township Board of Education.

## Television

3-2-1 Contact Programs: *Space Monday* (#301) and *Measurement Friday* (#310). Check with local public broadcasting stations for airing dates.

*Scientific American Frontiers– The World of Science:* PBS, 8:00 p.m., October 10, 1990.

Reprinted from *The Physics Teacher* **28**, 446-453, ©1990 American Association of Physics Teachers.

# Amusement Park Physics

## By Carole Escobar

$T$he use of amusement parks by physics classes has expanded enormously in the last few years. This spring, over ten thousand students were involved in Physics Day at the park my classes use. Other parks across the country have as many, and some more, students come to do physics activities on a special day. The reason this has become so popular is that the physics of the rides is simple enough to be handled at the introductory level. An analysis of some of the rides was given by John Roeder in the September 1975 issue of *The Physics Teacher* (**13** : 327).

Rides can be grouped in a number of ways. For example, there are rides that go in horizontal circles, others that go in vertical circles, and a whole category that are essentially falls of one kind or another. When teaching uniform circular motion I use the carousel (Fig. 1). Since all the horses travel at the same angular speed, $\omega$, the centripetal acceleration is directly related to the distance of the horse from the axis of rotation. At the park my students time the ride to find the frequency and they pace the diameter of the carousel. They can then verify that the acceleration varies as the radius by using an accelerometer while riding first one horse and then another at a different radius.

Another horizontal circle is executed by the swings on a rotating swing ride (Fig. 2). But this ride has the additional advantage of illustrating the vector addition of forces. The only forces acting on a swing rider are the tension in the chains and the weight of the rider. Since the swings travel in a circle, the resultant force is the centripetal force. A free body diagram shows that a measurement of the angle between the chains and the vertical central support should satisfy the relationship $\tan \theta = 4\pi^2 R/gT^2$. A swing ride model or the actual park ride can be used to verify this by measuring the period of rotation and the

Fig. 1. Carousel.

$$centripetal\ acceleration = \frac{v^2}{R} = \frac{4\pi^2 R}{T^2} = \omega^2 R$$

radius of rotation when the swing is in motion. One additional point is that the analysis predicts that the mass of the rider does not affect the angle at which the swings rotate.

**Carole Escobar** *received her B.A. from Barnard College and an M.A. from the State University of New York at Stony Brook, both in physics. She teaches, mainly physics, at Bellport High School on Long Island and is assistant editor of TPT. Her interest in the physics of amusement park rides dates from her inauguration of a Physics Day at a park in New Jersey almost ten years ago.*

Fig. 2. Swings.

Students are surprised to see that even empty swings are right in line with the loaded ones, just as predicted.

What physics does not predict is that the response of the rider's body is in the opposite direction to the applied

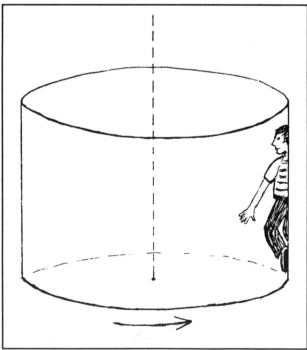

Fig. 3. Rotor.

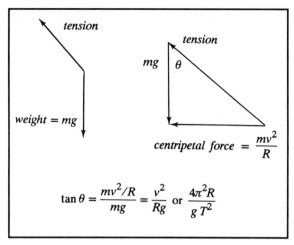

$$\tan \theta = \frac{mv^2/R}{mg} = \frac{v^2}{Rg} \text{ or } \frac{4\pi^2 R}{g T^2}$$

force as seen in the free body diagram. You do not feel the force as being in the direction a free body diagram predicts. When standing at rest, your body interprets the push of the floor against your feet as a downward force. It takes some doing to convince beginning students that, in fact, the floor, or seat of the chair, is pushing upward. Students "feel" a downward pull. In exactly the same way, a rider being pushed in toward the center of a rotating ride "feels" pushed outward. Free body diagrams implicitly use the frame of reference of the nonrotating observer. But the rider is in the rotating frame of reference and experiences an outward force.

The rotor (Fig. 3) is perhaps the ride that best illustrates this reversal. It is a rotating ride in which riders stand against a wall and find themselves stuck to the wall once the ride is up to speed. In practice it is easiest to make measurements if the ride is of the type that is open at the top. Students can pace the diameter before it begins to rotate and time the rotation from an observation walk above. They quickly see that the upward force opposing their weight is friction since the walls are usually indoor-outdoor carpeting or some other rough surface. The normal force is the centripetal push of the walls, and the analysis can be carried to the point of finding a coefficient of friction. (Unfortunately, the coefficient is not usually verifiable by some other

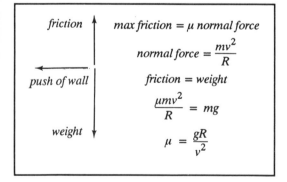

# Amusement Park Physics

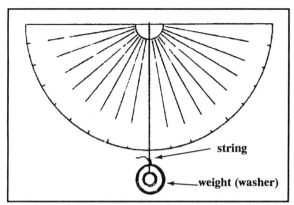

Fig. 4. Protractor accelerometer.

means.) When students doubt that friction is a force, the rotor ride is a convincing experience.

To verify the magnitude of the acceleration, students take accelerometers (Fig. 4) onto the ride. The hanging mass of an accelerometer swings outward toward the wall as if an outward force has been applied. An outward force is what the rider feels and so the accelerometer verifies the sensation. An observer on the ground sees the string from which the mass is hung applying an inward force and verifies that the force is centripetal. Both are right. Each is conducting the analysis from a different frame of reference. When discussing the rides I make it clear that the rider is in one frame of reference and the observer in another.

Vertical circles (Fig. 5) are harder to analyze since the weight vector goes from being in the same direction as the force applied by the track inside a vertical loop at the top,

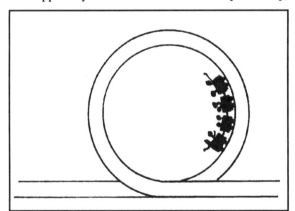

Fig. 5. Loop-the-loop.

| top | $\downarrow mg \downarrow track \downarrow \dfrac{mv^2}{R}$ | $mg + T = \dfrac{mv^2}{R}$ |
| --- | --- | --- |
| side | $\downarrow mg \leftarrow track \leftarrow \dfrac{mv^2}{R}$ | $T = \dfrac{mv^2}{R}$ |
| bottom | $\downarrow mg \uparrow track \uparrow \dfrac{mv^2}{R}$ | $T - mg = \dfrac{mv^2}{R}$ |

to being perpendicular to the track force halfway up, to being in the opposite direction from the track force at the bottom of the loop. On the other hand, having ridden a loop-the-loop roller coaster in the park, riders remember the changing sensation as a function of the position of the car. (That is, if they remember anything other than their terror. This is a good place to make it clear that students *do not have to ride*. My own experience has taught me that a terrified observer learns no physics. All measurements required of students can be made with both feet firmly on the ground. If they can ride, of course, they have these visceral memories to help them remember the physics.)

One ride that executes circular motion is shaped like a pirate boat (Fig. 6) that swings back and forth as a huge pendulum. Some versions have a counterweight and go all the way around. There are also rings of cages, in which riders stand, that start out rotating horizontally and then whirl in a vertical circle. At the top, riders feel almost as if they are falling free of the cage. At the bottom they feel squashed against the steel cage at their backs. Both of these feelings agree with the analysis of forces if you concentrate on finding the applied force. Usually, when circular motion in a vertical plane is discussed in class, the student is asked to do a free body diagram in various spots and show the resultant force. If the motion is uniform, only the direction of the resultant changes. But the body of a rider responds to the force applied by the track or cage rather than to the resultant force. At the top, since weight is helping to provide the centripetal force, the applied force may be very small and the rider feels almost "weightless." At the bottom, weight is in the opposite direction to the necessary centripetal force and so the push of the ride is larger and the rider feels "heavier." Your body does not distinguish between the usual force due to gravity and the push of the wall. Both are interpreted as weight. An

Fig. 6. Pirate boat.

Amusement Park Physics

Fig. 7. Enterprise.

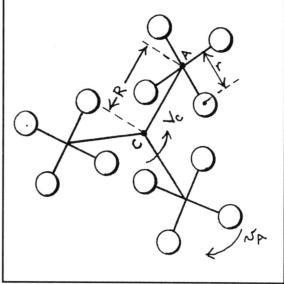

Fig. 9a. Scorpion.

accelerometer taken on the ride will show a large acceleration at the bottom and a very small one at the top since it is showing the applied, not resultant force.

An additional bit of physics in the pirate boat version that does not go "over-the-top" is the method by which it is propelled. Most often there are motor-driven tires below the boat that simply press against the bottom to push it. One set rotates forward, the other set backwards, and they are raised or lowered to match the motion of the boat. Because the boat makes contact with the tires only at the bottom of the swing, energy is fed into the pendulum at its resonant frequency and the amplitude of the swing in-

creases although the motion of the tires is constant. To brake, the tires that are moving in the opposite direction to the boat are raised. The simplicity of the whole thing is a welcome antidote to the impression that all mechanical devices are computerized and too complex to be easily understood.

Then there are the rides that incorporate both horizontal and vertical circles in the same ride. One (Fig. 7) has hanging cars that swing out as the ride speeds up in a horizontal plane, and then the entire apparatus is tilted until the rotation is in a vertical plane. Students can feel the difference between the two planes in that the sensation is the same all the way around the horizontal circle, but each position has a distinct feeling once the whole thing is in the vertical plane. There is also a "snake" ride (Fig. 8) in which the circle is draped across hills and valleys. Riders are thrown against the outward side of the slippery seat and go from feeling light-headed at the top of hills to being crushed at the bottom. Quick-thinking boys sit on the outside of the girl in this old-fashioned ride.

The hardest motion to analyze on an introductory level is the dual axis rotation (Fig. 9a). A small car, typically two-person, rotates about an axis, which is on the end of a long arm. The arm rotates about the center of the entire ride. Each person then goes in a circle, which is itself moving in a circle. Astronomy teachers use this to illustrate the motion of a moon.

One thing students can do is time the independent motions and measure the radii. Now they can do a vector analysis by plotting the positions of the car from the center of the whole ride (Fig. 9b). Next they draw the radial displacement

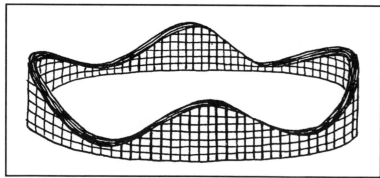

Fig. 8. Hills and valleys circular ride.

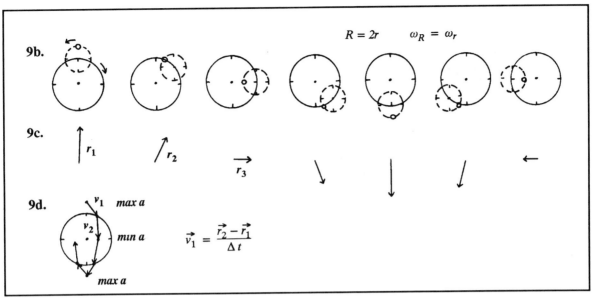

$$R = 2r \qquad \omega_R = \omega_r$$

**9b.**

**9c.**

$\vec{r}_1$    $\vec{r}_2$    $\vec{r}_3$

**9d.**

$v_1$   *max a*

$v_2$   *min a*

$\vec{v}_1 = \dfrac{\vec{r}_2 - \vec{r}_1}{\Delta t}$

*max a*

**Fig. 9b–d.**

vectors for equal time intervals (Fig. 9c). These are proportional to the radial velocities with respect to Earth. As you can see in the diagram, the maximum *changes* in velocity occur when the cars are farthest from the center, and the smallest accelerations occur when the cars are nearest the center. Figures 9b–d were drawn for the simple case in which the two frequencies of rotation are equal, and maximum acceleration occurs twice for each revolution about the center of the whole ride, always in the same two places. Notice that the two rotations are in opposite sense, one clockwise, one counterclockwise. Try drawing the same displacement diagram for rotations in the same sense and observe that in the case of $f_R = f_r$ the car remains at constant radius, thus producing no thrills.

A word of warning. Addition of the vectors for the instantaneous velocity of the car relative to the end of the arm and the instantaneous velocity of the end of the arm relative to the center at the extreme positions does not yield the correct result of maximum accelerations at the furthest points and minimum accelerations at the innermost positions. A calculus approach is needed since the velocity is continuously changing in both magnitude and direction. On the other hand, analysis of the force needed to go around the end of the arm and the force needed to go around the center of the ride makes it clear that the forces add at the outermost position and are in opposite directions at the innermost position. So the outermost acceleration is going to be greater than the innermost. At the park, students can verify that the rotation about the end of the arm is always opposite to the rotation about the center of the ride, and riders can feel the crush at the outermost position and the easing up of that force as the car nears the center of the ride.

Falling rides range from a free fall tower (Fig. 10) that turns the falling carriage from vertical to horizontal through a large radius curve in order to stop it, to water slides and downhill toboggan-type

**Fig. 10. Free fall.**

**Fig. 11. Water slide.**

rides (Fig. 11). The tower is truly a free fall for about one second. The time of fall and the distance of this vertical portion of the ride can be measured and the $\frac{1}{2}gt^2$ relationship for distance in free fall verified. The only hitch is to be sure students recognize that the curve is not to be included in the measurement of distance fallen. By measuring the horizontal distance over which braking takes place, they can compute the deceleration as well. It is interesting to note that this whole ride is heavily computer-monitored and in particular that the braking portion has to have a force-sensing device, not just a speed-sensing mechanism, in order to vary the force applied to the carriage as a function of the mass of the riders. The deceleration at the park we use is just about 10 m/s$^2$.

How about roller coasters? (Fig. 12) Depending on the particular configuration, roller coasters can be used to illustrate the addition of forces in vertical loops and horizontal circles, as well as conservation of mechanical energy. Of course energy is not conserved by a roller coaster train rolling down hill. We know, and the students know, that friction eats up some of the gravitational potential available at the top. But if you measure the heights of the first two hills you can estimate the loss of energy as a function of track length. (Notice I said estimate. Any measurement taken in the park has a healthy component of error. That is part of the lesson for my students. Estimate your margin of error and then decide if your results agree within your margin.) One look at a roller coaster that has a loop higher than the station from which the train starts and a physics

student should know that the train has to be catapulted from the station.

We use an accelerometer that can also be used as a sextant (Fig. 13). Since students know the length of their pace, they can measure heights by triangulation. Measuring the heights of rides is a whole lesson in itself.

A valuable lesson in the measurements taken on the roller coaster is that in measuring the speed of a train students are finding the average speed at a point on the track. What they feel on the ride is the instantaneous value. People in the first car have a very different ride from the people in the last as they pass over the same point in the track. All that gets smoothed into an average speed by measuring the total length of the train and dividing by the time it takes to cross a point on the track. The difference between average and instantaneous speed takes on an "Aha" quality as soon as students think about the roller coaster.

Another point that needs to be made is that the vertical loops on roller coasters are not circular. We all do the problem that asks from what height must an object be released in order to just make the track at the top of a frictionless, circular loop-the-loop. If you change the question and ask what is the force that must be applied to the car by the track in order to have it just make the top, a practical consideration emerges (Fig. 14). Assume that the car is moving at the speed at the top at which the centripetal force is equal to the weight of the car. This is

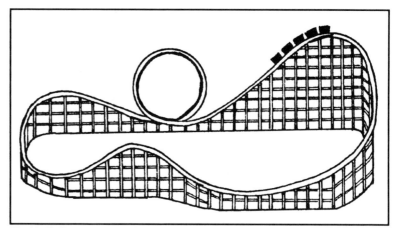

**Fig. 12. Roller coaster with vertical loop and two hills.**

# Amusement Park Physics

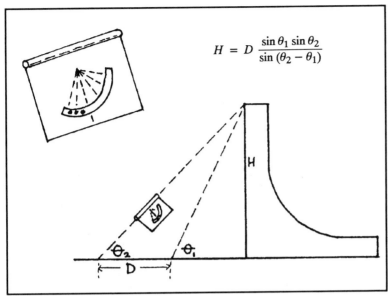

$$H = D \, \frac{\sin \theta_1 \sin \theta_2}{\sin (\theta_2 - \theta_1)}$$

**Fig. 13. PASCO horizontal accelerometer.**

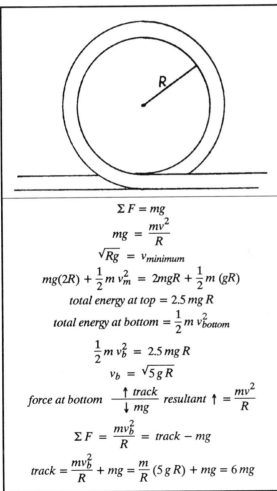

$$\Sigma F = mg$$
$$mg = \frac{mv^2}{R}$$
$$\sqrt{Rg} = v_{minimum}$$
$$mg(2R) + \frac{1}{2}m\,v_m^2 = 2mgR + \frac{1}{2}m\,(gR)$$

*total energy at top = 2.5 mg R*

*total energy at bottom* $= \frac{1}{2}m\,v_{bottom}^2$

$$\frac{1}{2}m\,v_b^2 = 2.5\,mg\,R$$
$$v_b = \sqrt{5\,g\,R}$$

*force at bottom* $\dfrac{\uparrow \; track}{\downarrow \; mg}$ *resultant* $\uparrow = \dfrac{mv^2}{R}$

$$\Sigma F = \frac{mv_b^2}{R} = track - mg$$

$$track = \frac{mv_b^2}{R} + mg = \frac{m}{R}(5\,g\,R) + mg = 6\,mg$$

**Fig. 14. Velocities and forces in circular loop.**

the minimum speed at the top to keep the car on the track. No force is being applied by the track to the car at the top of the loop, but the car is not leaving the track either. Now assume the track to be frictionless(!). Conservation of energy analysis gives the speed at the bottom to be about two-and-a-quarter times greater than at the top. Since the track at the bottom must provide both the centripetal force and support the weight of the train, the total force applied by the track to the rider at the bottom turns out to be six times the rider's weight. This is such a large force that passengers are uncomfortable to say the least. In reality, since the track is not frictionless, the speed at the bottom would be less than in the ideal case, but for safety's sake, the speed at the top is actually higher than the minimum, so that, even factoring in friction, the force applied at the bottom on a truly circular loop is too large for comfort.

The high acceleration, high force at the bottom of the loop is avoided by using what is called a clothoid loop (Fig. 15) in place of a circular loop. The clothoid has a smaller radius of curvature at the top than at the bottom. Because the loop closes down, the minimum speed at the top is smaller than it would be if the radius were constant, and so a slower ride at the bottom can still provide enough speed at the top. Riders still have the sensation of weightlessness at the top, but the slower speed at the bottom makes for a more comfortable ride. Also, note that real vertical loops on a roller coaster have curved track leading into the loop. You do not go from a straight, level (infinite radius) track into the loop. Instead, the car dips down into a very large radius curve that leads into the upward slope of the loop.

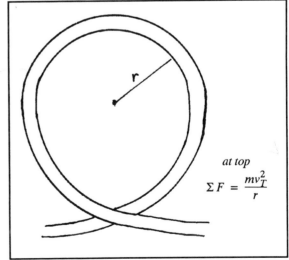

*at top*
$$\Sigma F = \frac{mv_T^2}{r}$$

**Fig. 15. Clothoid loop.**

This also allows for less acceleration, less change in the direction of the velocity over a short time interval. Instead of suddenly going into an upward curve, the car starts into the curve far back on the track.

Careful analysis of the loop is beyond the scope of an introductory course, but you can analyze the shape of a roller coaster's first hill in detail. Project a slide of the first hill onto the blackboard, and measure the coordinates of the track in two dimensions. Within a reasonable margin of error you can show that the coordinates fit the equation of a parabola. By this point in the course you have probably made the analysis of a horizontally projected object and students know that the path followed ideally takes the shape of a parabola. The feeling that you are falling on the downslope of the roller coaster hill is carefully engineered. Since you are traveling in a parabolic path, you feel as if you are falling. Students are reassured to know that roller coasters have two sets of wheels, one on top of the rails and one below the rails. If the track is well designed, there will be little wear on the track on the downslopes, but the car is still firmly attached.

Of course this is only some of the physics that can be taught at the amusement park. Some teachers time the roller coaster's ride up the first hill and ask students to compute the power needed, assuming some average weight of the train and its riders. Fermi questions abound. (How many flowers are blooming in the park today? How many paid admissions were there today? What percent of the total time in the park is spent on line?) Some estimate the total electrical power needed by the park. You can frame questions about momentum, qualitative on the bumper cars or boats and quantitative on the water slide, by timing the splash and measuring the speed of the boat before and after the splash.

At first it seems contradictory to use an amusement park for serious academic work. Both students and other faculty tend not to take me seriously when they first hear about a field trip to the amusement park. Yet the physics of the rides is simple. I can tell from the excellent questions that students ask on the bus ride home that they do have their brains in gear in the park. The experience reinforces what they have learned in class, brings up new questions, counters the prevailing myth that physics is abstract (accessible only by the brightest), and, best of all, integrates enjoyment and intellectual activity. Physics in the amusement park is simple, it's real, and it's fun. ◆

*Editor's Note:* The sketches in this article were drawn by Arthlyn Ferguson, who for many years was the managing editor of *TPT*.

Reprinted from *The Physics Teacher* **13**, 327-332, ©1975 American Association of Physics Teachers.

# Physics and the Amusement Park

## John L. Roeder

What does physics have to do with an amusement park? For the millions of people who visit amusement parks every year, physics is probably the last thing on their minds. They are more interested in taking a thrilling ride, possibly wondering how "scary" it will be. But to those who have often wondered this, physics has the answer.

Although the roller coaster has become a classic example of energy conversions in a mechanical system,[1] we must make a more detailed investigation of the rides at an amusement park in order to determine how scary they are. The key here is the acceleration produced on the riders. For, as one learns from studying motion in an accelerated reference frame, these accelerations subject the riders to forces. According to the general theory of relativity, these reference frame forces are indistinguishable from gravitational forces. Indeed, they are the basis of "artificial gravity" as it is and will be employed in our exploration of space.

I first analyzed the forces of an accelerated frame of reference on an amusement park ride several years ago while passing a carnival. I spied a ride that I believe was called the "dip." It consisted of two cages mounted at opposite ends of a system of girders which rotated in a vertical circle. With such an arrangement, the rider is upside down at the top.

Watching this ride from the ground always suggested that it must be a terrifying experience. But then I found myself timing its rotations: about 3 sec apiece (and hence an angular velocity of about 2 rad/sec). Next I estimated the radius to be 5 m and calculated the centripetal acceleration of the riders, according to the familiar expression

$$a = \omega^2 R \qquad (1)$$

where $a$ is the centripetal acceleration, $\omega$ is the angular velocity, and $R$ is the radius. The result was 20 m/sec², about 2 g's (twice the acceleration due to earth's gravity). Since this means an artificial gravitational field twice as strong as the earth's, directed radially outward, I realized that I had sized up this ride all wrong! Instead of feeling most terrified at being upside down at the top, one should feel the least terrified there. The net gravitational field there should be

**John L. Roeder** *received his A.B. from Washington University and his Ph.D. from Princeton University. After teaching physics at Transylvania University, Dr. Roeder moved to The Calhoun School in New York City, where he has been teaching and developing an individualized curriculum in physics and chemistry for grades 6-12 since 1973. (The Calhoun School, New York, New York 10024)*

about 1 g — upward — so the rider in his upside down position should feel completely normal!

This can be represented mathematically as follows. The acceleration of the riders is represented vectorially as

$$\vec{a} = -\omega^2 R \sin(\omega t + \phi)\,\vec{k} - \omega^2 R \cos(\omega t + \phi)\,\vec{j} \qquad (2)$$

where $t$ is time, $\phi$ an arbitrary phase angle, and $j$ and $k$ are unit horizontal and vertical vectors, respectively. The net gravitational field felt by the riders — formed by the sum of the earth's gravitational field and the artificial field resulting from their acceleration — is then

$$\vec{g}' = [-g + \omega^2 R \sin(\omega t + \phi)]\,k + \omega^2 R \cos(\omega t + \phi)\,\vec{j} \qquad (3)$$

This vector summation for the special case we have considered ($\omega^2 R = 2g$) is pictured in Fig. 1; here one can see that the magnitude of $\vec{g}'$ varies from g at the top to 3g at the bottom. The horizontal and vertical components of $\vec{g}'$ are pictured for the same case (and $\phi = 0$) in Fig. 2.

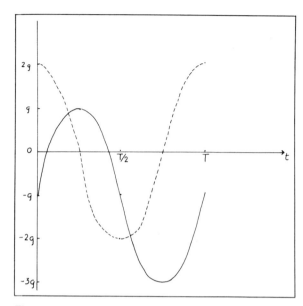

Fig. 2. Horizontal (dashed line) and vertical (solid line) components of the net gravitational field felt by riders on the dip as a function of time for a full cycle.

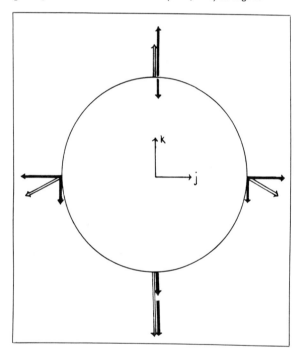

Fig. 1. The net gravitational field felt by riders at various positions on the dip is indicated by hollow arrows. This is the sum of the earth's gravitational field (solid arrows directed downward) and the artificial field resulting from the dip's rotation (solid arrows directed radially outward).

Although I still haven't taken a ride on the dip, I have enjoyed a variety of other amusement park rides since my interest in them as an application of physics has been reawakened recently. In fact, I took a group of students on one classic ride for a learning experience. This was the "hell hole," a cylinder about 2 m in radius and about 3 m high. "Place your heels and stretch your arms out against the wall," the man said before he started the cylinder spinning in rotations I would later measure to require only 1.4 sec each. These were the only safety precautions; artificial

gravity took care of the rest. And when he lowered the floor we were almost literally glued to the wall.

After our ride on the hell hole, we calculated what our acceleration had been. It turned out to be 40.2 m/sec², about 4 g's. We could also calculate the minimum coefficient of friction needed for us to stay glued to the wall when the floor was lowered. Friction would need to balance the earth's downward gravitational force and thus would need to be at least a quarter of the radially outward force due to artificial gravity. The minimum coefficient of friction must therefore be the ratio of the former to the latter, or 0.25.

A variation of the hell hole is the more frequently-encountered "roundup." Typical values for this ride are a radius of 5 m and a period of rotation of 4 sec, leading to a centripetal acceleration of 12.3 m/sec², a little more than 1 g. Here, with a smaller artificial gravitational field, the riders must be chained into position. In fact, were the roundup operated in the same way as the hell hole, it would be a comfortable place to take a nap (not a bad idea if you're on an all day outing!). For the net result would be a constant gravitational field with magnitude of only around 1.6 g, in contrast to almost three times as much on the hell hole. (See Fig. 3.)

So, to add greater thrill to the roundup, it is tilted — up to as much as 60° from the vertical. The result is a varying acceleration — still a pleasant experience, although I found the bobbing up and down of my Adam's apple somewhat annoying. In fact, this seems to be a general guiding principle for amusement park rides: the important feature is not the magnitude of the inertial frame forces to which they subject the riders (except in the hell hole, where it is so large), but rather the ways in which and the rates with which these forces change. Thus, the amusement park suggests a physical role for the third derivative of position with respect to time.

Let us now examine the roundup in more quantitative detail. With respect to a primed coordinate system tilted

328

Fig. 3. The Roundup

Great Adventure, Jackson, NJ

along with the roundup at an angle $\psi$ from the vertical (Fig. 4), the acceleration is

$$\vec{a} = -\omega^2 R \cos(\omega t + \phi)\,\vec{i}' - \omega^2 R \sin(\omega t + \phi)\,\vec{j}' \qquad (4)$$

where $\vec{i}'$ and $\vec{j}'$ are unit horizontal vectors and all other symbols have the same meaning as in Eq. (1) and (2). With respect to the same coordinate system, the net gravitational field felt by riders on the roundup is then

$$\vec{g}' = -g \cos \psi \, \vec{k}' + \omega^2 R \sin(\omega t + \phi)\,\vec{j}' \\ + [\,\omega^2 R \cos(\omega t + \phi) - g \sin \psi\,]\,\vec{i}' \qquad (5)$$

The magnitude of this field is

$$g' = [\,g^2 + \omega^4 R^2 - 2g\omega^2 R \sin \psi \cos(\omega t + \phi)\,]^{1/2} \qquad (6)$$

It is seen to vary from a minimum of $(g^2 + \omega^4 R^2 - 2g\omega^2 R \cos \psi)^{1/2}$ to a maximum of $(g^2 + \omega^4 R^2 + 2g\omega^2 R \cos \psi)^{1/2}$. In fact, the roundup can be

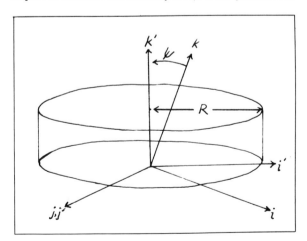

Fig. 4. Schematic diagram of the roundup, showing tilted coordinate system.

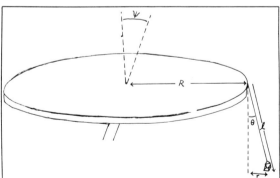

Fig. 5. Schematic diagram of the swings. The swings are chairs suspended by chains of length $l$ from a rotating disc of radius $R$ tilted by angle $\psi$ from the vertical.

Amusement Park Physics

Fig. 6.
The Swings
("Flying Wave")

Great Adventure, Jackson, NJ

considered to be a generalization incorporating both the dip *and* the hell hole. It becomes a dip when $\psi = 90°$ and a hell hole when $\psi = 0°$.

A variation of the roundup is the "swings," a set of chairs suspended by chains from a tilted rotating disc (Fig. 6). The chains suspending the chairs will hang — like plumb lines — in the direction of the net gravitational field. This is conveniently expressed by the "swing angle" — between the chains and the perpendicular to the rotating disc, denoted by $\theta$ in Fig. 5. The secant of this angle is the ratio of the net gravitational field to its component perpendicular to the disc, which we have already calculated in equations (5) and (6):

$$\operatorname{Sec} \theta = [g^2 + \omega^4 R^2 - 2g\omega^2 R \sin \psi \cos(\omega t + \theta)]^{1/2}/g \cos \psi \quad (7)$$

If the length of the chains is $l$ (as in Fig. 6) the result is to increase the radius of rotation by a time-dependent amount:

$$r = l \sin \theta \quad (8)$$

Therefore, the results we have derived for the roundup are also valid for the swings if we replace $R$ by $R + r$.

Because the swings, with the same radius as the roundup, have a much longer period (7 sec), their centripetal acceleration is significantly less — only about 4 m/sec$^2$, or less than ½ g. The "tilt" of the swings is also less, about 20°. This leads to swing angles ranging from near 0° to 38°, as are in fact observed. Because of its smaller centripetal acceleration the swings are less "scary" than the roundup. If the swings had the same period as the roundup, the swing angle would range from 42° to 58°. If they had the same tilt as the roundup as well, this range would be expanded — from 34° to 76°. In either case, these large swing angles would make the swings "scary" indeed, especially with long chains. (See Fig. 6.)

Large swing angles are, in fact, the object of another type of ride, frequently known as the "Swiss bob." Here a train of cars moves up and down "mountains" along a circular path with a typical radius of 5 m, completing a circuit about every four and a half seconds. There are two versions of this ride: one, with cars suspended from above and free to hang in the direction of the net gravitational field; the other, with cars supported from below by a suspension system which allows them to tilt to a certain extent under the influence of the net gravitational field.

In the Swiss bob the "mountains" play the same role in varying the swing angle as tilting the rotating disc from which the swings are suspended. But although the underlying physical principle is the same, differences in actual geometrical configurations make it more straightforward to analyze the Swiss bob in another way. Each mountain and valley can be viewed as a portion of a vertical circle, with a consequent artificial gravitational field induced in the vertical as well as horizontal direction. At the top of the mountain, the artificial gravitational field is directed upward as well as outward. Here a swing angle of 90° can be achieved by choosing the radius of curvature of the mountain ($\rho$) so that the vertical part of the artificial field exactly cancels the field due to earth's gravity. This means

$$v^2/\rho = (\omega R)^2/\rho = g \quad (9)$$

where $v$ is the Swiss bob's linear speed. Using observed values of $\omega$, $R$, and g, Eq. (9) yields a value of $\rho = 1$ m.

The final type of ride we shall consider embodies two circular motions, like Ptolemaic epicycles moving along their deferents. Of importance here is not only the radius, speed, and acceleration of each circular motion but also the relationship between them. In particular, the relationship between the speed $V$ along the larger circle (deferent) and the speed $v$ in the smaller circle (epicycle) relative to the

330

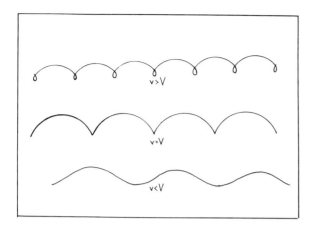

Fig. 7. Three different types of epicyclic motion are possible, depending upon the relationship between the speed in the epicycle ($v$) and the speed along the deferent ($V$).

Fig. 8a. The Pretty Monster in motion.

Fig. 8b. The Pretty Monster at rest.

larger distinguishes among the three cases pictured in Fig. 7. As one can tell by examining the data in Table I for the "monster" (Fig. 8) and the "tilt-a-whirl" (Fig. 9), two rides based on this principle, the last of the three cases in Fig. 7 is usually achieved in actuality. (And those who believe these rides to be "scary" should remember that this case provides the "smoothest" ride.)

While the monster and tilt-a-whirl share the combination of two circular motions in common, they also differ in much the same way as the Swiss bob differs from

Fig. 9.
The Tilt-a-Whirl ("Calypso") in motion.

SEPTEMBER 1975

331

Amusement Park Physics

97

| Ride | | Period (sec) | Radius (m) | Speed (m/sec) | Angular Speed (rad/sec) | Acceleration (m/sec$^2$) |
|---|---|---|---|---|---|---|
| dip | | 3 | 5 | 10.4 | 2.1 | 21.9 |
| hell hole | | 1.4 | 2 | 9.0 | 4.5 | 40.2 |
| roundup | | 4 | 5 | 7.9 | 1.6 | 12.3 |
| swings | | 7 | 5 | 4.5 | 0.9 | 4.0 |
| Swiss bob (both versions) | | 4.5 | 5 | 7.0 | 1.4 | 9.8 |
| monster | large | 10 | 5 | 3.1 | 0.6 | 2.0 |
| | small | 3.5 | 1.5 | 2.7 | 1.8 | 4.8 |
| tilt-a-whirl | large | 5 | 3 | 3.8 | 1.2 | 4.7 |
| | small | 2.5 | 1 | 2.5 | 2.5 | 6.3 |

the swings. The monster and some tilt-a-whirls incorporate a sinusoidal vertical motion like that produced by the mountains of the Swiss bob. Other types of tilt-a-whirl are simply mounted on a tilted platform.

Data from all the rides we have discussed are summarized in Table I. If we exclude the swings and consider only the more "thrilling" rides, we see that the conjecture we made above in discussing the roundup has been borne out. The key to amusement park rides is not only the magnitude of the accelerations they give their riders but also the ways in which and the rates with which these accelerations change. The lower the magnitude of individual accelerations, the more complex the way in which they are combined.

I wish to thank Ms. Pamela Bryant of public relations at Great Adventure, Jackson, NJ, for her cooperation in providing photographs of many of the rides I used in the course of my "research."

### Reference

1. A. Einstein and L. Infeld, *The Evolution of Physics* (Simon and Schuster, New York, 1950), pp. 44-47.

Reprinted from *The Physics Teacher* **22**, 361-367, ©1984 American Association of Physics Teachers.

# A physics laboratory at Six Flags Over Georgia

Most of us who teach physics agree that *doing* physics is essential to any student's understanding of basic principles, and we agree that "doing" includes solving problems and laboratory work. The challenge is to generate problems and laboratory experiences that have significance to students.

It is our belief that this significance originates in using things that are familiar and scaled to human size. As a student matures in his understanding of physics he begins to realize that the excitement comes from the study of things at extreme scales — subatomic and cosmological, but until such sophistication develops, our point of contact with him is in things of *familiar* and *ordinary* size.

To some extent this observation is hindsight because what we're about to describe originated as a dare from one of the present authors to another. It was only as we explored the possibilities in the light of our understanding of fundamental teaching principles and a number of years of physics teaching experience that size and familiarity began to seem so important.

Thus, the results are presented with enthusiasm but also with the realization that there are as many ways to teach physics effectively as there are capable teachers, motivated students, and supportive school administrators.

### Background

The project began in the fall of 1975 when two of the authors, Page and Taylor, were considering various methods of bringing physics closer to the high school students' experience with the physical world. We hoped to provide a year-end opportunity for students to apply and to master concepts which they had confronted and studied during the first year physics course at the Baylor School.

Students encounter these concepts in the usual ways. These included typical classroom laboratories, laboratory experiences outside the classroom, lectures, a variety of homework assignments from textbook problems to term papers, talks by visiting scientists, and films. The fundamental emphasis of the first course is to provide students the ability to explain natural phenomena using approximate and exact measurements. (By "approximate" we mean "order of magnitude estimates" while by "exact" we mean "measurements made with the aid of instruments.")

During the 15 years one of us, Taylor, has been at Baylor, the number of physics students has remained relatively constant, averaging 75 students per

**GEORGE TAYLOR**
**JOSEPH PAGE**
**MURRY BENTLEY**
**DIANA LOSSNER**
*The Baylor School, Chattanooga, Tennessee 37401*

**George Taylor** *has taught at Baylor since 1969. For the past ten years he has also served as the Chairman of the Science Department.*

**Joe Page** *taught at Baylor 1973-78. He has been a programmer and data systems analyst and is now a manager at BellSouth Services in Atlanta.*

**Murry Bentley** *taught at Baylor 1980-83. He is currently a graduate student in Physics at Johns Hopkins University.*

**Diana Lossner** *was at Baylor 1978-80. Her current address is Route 3, Box 343, Adamsville, Tennessee 38310.*

Amusement Park Physics

## Table I

### Number of students who have gone to Six Flags with Baylor team

| Date | Total | Baylor Students | Baylor AP Students[3] | Other School Students |
|------|-------|-----------------|----------------------|----------------------|
| May 22, 1976 | 40 | 40 | - | - |
| Apr. 23, 1977 | 59 | 59 | - | - |
| May 22, 1978 | 90 | 69 | - | 21[1] |
| Apr. 28, 1979 | 92 | 66 | 11 | 15[1] |
| May 10, 1980 | 70 | 55 | 10 | 5[1] |
| May 9, 1981 | 52 | 47 | 5 | - |
| May 8, 1982 | 81 | 55 | 5 | 21[2] |
| Apr. 30, 1983 | 88 | 49 | 10 | 29[2] |
| Apr. 28, 1984 | 35 | 30 | 5 | - |

1. These students were from two schools in Chattanooga, Tennessee; Girls' Preparatory School and Notre Dame High School.
2. These students were from Norcross High School, Norcross, Georgia.
3. Baylor AP students are in an AP-level physics class which is a second-year physics class. These students have a somewhat different set of questions. These students experienced Six Flags the previous year and are on a second trip. Their set of questions will not be discussed.

year, and approximately 65% of each graduating class has been in physics. For the past several years the physics class has been a mixture primarily of juniors and seniors with a small number of sophomores. The second teacher in the department has changed several times. Page was here five years, Lossner for two, and Bentley for three.

Six-hundred-seven students have participated in this project. Of these students, 91 from other schools went with Baylor's physics students for the day. They have been from two area high schools — each of which has gone with us two different years, and in 1982 and 1983, an Atlanta area high school physics class participated with us. Table I shows the number of students involved each year.

The project itself is to use a major Atlanta area amusement park, Six Flags Over Georgia, as the setting for a one-day laboratory exercise and evaluation of the students' understanding of physics.[1] The excursion to Six Flags is not a requirement of the course, although it is encouraged. It takes place on a Saturday; the students must pay for their tickets, bus, and food. It provides bragging rights and great war stories for dates, friends, and younger students. In late April or May there are many conflicts which cannot be avoided; e.g., athletic contests, school plays, proms, Saturday jobs, etc. In spite of these, well over half of our students have made the trek each spring. For those who cannot go, an alternate exercise is provided the following week.

### Concepts and goals

Prior to the first laboratory at Six Flags, Page and Taylor outlined a number of special issues before considering the goals and questions to be given the students. We considered:
1. What concepts should students have mastered?
2. Could students give a qualitative description of the

phenomena (in this case a Six Flags ride)?
3. What physical quantities could be measured? And, could fairly rigid standards be applied to encourage quality, quantity and consistency of measurements?
4. What had to be estimated?
5. Could students function in the very nonacademic atmosphere of Six Flags?

Using the initial answers to these questions, Page and Taylor wrote a set of problems for use in the spring of 1976. As each year's data (student results) have been accumulated, we have made an effort to improve the following year's teaching where results badly missed expectations. The goal of this exercise, the application of basic physical principles by the students has remained unchanged; the particular wording has varied from year to year as we have continually attempted to state the questions more clearly. To summarize those principles being tested we created three categories: Primary concepts, secondary concepts, and general techniques.

### A. Primary concepts
1. Straight-line kinematics, graphing, and the connection between graphs.
2. Conservation of mechanical energy. Evaluation of kinetic energy, gravitational potential energy, and their connections.
3. Newton's laws of motion; summation of forces, and free-body diagrams.
4. Circular motion.
5. Conservation of momentum; vector addition.

### B. Secondary concepts
1. Electrical energy and conservation of energy.
2. Frictional forces and work done by frictional forces.
3. Complete electrical circuits.
4. Frames of reference and retrograde motion.

### C. General techniques
1. Qualitative explanation of phenomena.
2. "Fermi questions" and order of magnitude estimates.
3. Organization of data and of information.
4. Presentation of information.
5. Measuring techniques

### Unusual opportunities for students

In many ways the lab at Six Flags is far more difficult than an ordinary lab or group of labs; it is tough to concentrate on conservation of momentum in the middle of a mass of people running by with balloons and cotton candy. On the other hand, our students are told — both by us and by last year's students — the type questions to expect and generally what will happen. This lowers anxiety levels and "pre-lab nerves." The detailed information given to students is shown in Figs. 1 and 2. Figure 1, "General Information for Six Flags Trip" is given to students approximately one week prior to departure; Fig. 2, "General Instructions and Information" is distributed 10 to 15 minutes before arriving at Six Flags. The questions — one per page — are stapled together with the instructions to form a booklet. All of the students work — data and answers — are written on these pages.

A perceived difficulty is that there is no teacher standing by with help and information. Students go in all directions and only chance encounters with teachers occur

**General information for Six Flags trip**

Be on your assigned bus in parking lot in front of Barks Hall at 7:17 a.m., Saturday, 8 May 1982.
The bus *will not* wait if you are late!
You will ride the *same bus* to and from Six Flags.
When we arrive at Six Flags, you will be given the questions.
Work with your lab group (two or three students) to take data with which to answer questions. Once you have the data needed, write your individual answer on your question book. *Answers are not to be a group effort!*
Mr. Bentley and Dr. Taylor will be in front of or in the Plantation House Restaurant at 12:00 and by the Great Gasp at 2:00, in case you have questions.
Be by the gate leading to bus at 5:19 p.m. *Again, do not be LATE!!!*
After everyone is on the bus, the questions will be collected.
REMEMBER – this is a *large part* of the term grade – do a good job!

**Equipment you will need on 8 May 1982**

1. Pencils
2. List of formulae and constants (lists may be shared in lab group)
3. Small ruler
4. Pocket full of assorted, simple, useful junk (value less than $3.14)
5. Money to buy your lunch.

**Forbidden equipment**

1. Any books
2. Electronic calculators
3. Surveyor's transit, etc.

**Fig. 1.**

**PHYSICS LABORATORY**

**SIX FLAGS**
**8 MAY 1982**

**General instructions and information**

1. Questions are to be answered by each person individually.
2. Record data in this booklet.
   a. Carefully explain *how* and *what* measurements were made.
   b. Distinguish clearly between measurements and calculations.
3. Give explanations and show all your work.
4. There are 6 problems, each has a value of 10 points.

Name ______________________

Lab group members ______________________

**Fig. 2.** The cover sheet for the booklet of questions

during the day. When approached with specific questions, we try to dispense verbal placeboes – this is the students' day to show what they can do!

Besides the amusement-park atmosphere and the lack of direct supervision, the students face a number of situations that are not easily duplicated in a classroom laboratory: There are no detailed instructions, no cookbook information, no equations for plug-in numbers. There is only the question about the physics of the ride.

Thus, the student (or small team of students) must:

1. Decide what the relevant variables are, i.e., what measurements must be made.
2. Decide how to make these measurements. For example, one question necessitates knowledge of the height of the Scream Machine (a very large roller coaster). Students must measure it without either climbing the apparatus or taking the quick and somewhat hazardous route of asking an attendant, although a number ask anyway. (Some attendants are willing to give numbers – a different number to each group asking!)
3. Take several measurements to obtain a reasonable average.
4. Organize their information and display all the data.
5. Explain the method of acquiring the data.
6. Immediately present results. All papers are returned as students board the bus at the end of the day.

Careful observation of phenomena, application of techniques and skills to acquire measurements, analysis of the data, and explanation of the results are the goals for the students. (We also hope students spend time enjoying themselves. A student's team working fairly diligently can finish in roughly one-half a day leaving the other half for fun. This is an individual decision for the students.) Internal consistency and reasonableness of results are more important than whether or not the answer is correct.

### Description of evaluation process

Each problem is assigned a grade from zero to ten. One of us grades the first three questions while the other grades the last three. Papers are read without knowing students' names or class and are graded one problem at a time. The order of grading is probably not sufficiently randomized to protect papers from fatigue but, because of the procedures followed, we feel that there is reasonable continuity and objectivity in the grading of each particular question for a particular year.

There is less consistency in comparing grades from one year to the next because of different graders, changes in the manner of asking the questions, and changes in partial credit schemes.

In general we were and are looking for the students' ability to make sufficient measurements and their ability to describe the process by which they make measurements and arrived at numerical conclusions. Particular criteria for each question will now be discussed.

### Questions and student responses

In this section we present selected questions and responses from throughout the nine years of this exercise to illustrate our method and some examples and evaluation of the students' work.

**Fig. 3.** Students (1980) answering questions with Scream Machine in background.

**Fig. 4.** Two students (1977) measuring the elevation of the Great Gasp.

**Problem 1**

Make a list of physical quantities observed at Six Flags. Fill in the following table. Check or fill in the appropriate columns. (List each physical quantity *only* once.)

Physical Location Scalar Vector How would you measure
quantity                                    directions for vector
                                             quantities? (Briefly)

This question has appeared twice, first in 1976 and again in 1982. Its purpose was to stimulate reconsideration:
   1. of the types of physical quantities studied during the year,
   2. of the fact that physical quantities can be classified as vectors and scalars,
   3. of the necessity to associate a direction in space with a vector.

Of the 1982 class, a large number (33%) did an excellent job, scoring 9 or better. The average grade for all students was 7.5. Both the good papers (9's and 10's) and the average ones typically listed from 8 to 12 quantities and properly identified them as vectors or scalars. The difference between the two groups was apparent in the assignment of directions in space to vectors.

**Problem 2** applies to the Great American Scream Machine (This is a very big roller coaster.)
   A. Discuss qualitatively the energy transformation in one complete trip. Specifically, consider the energy change from the loading area to the first peak and then the change from this point to the end of the ride. Are there energy inputs and losses in one trip?
   B. What measurements must be made to evaluate the maximum potential energy of the coaster? Carefully make these measurements and record results.

   C. Calculate the maximum potential energy of the coaster. Where is the coaster with this potential energy? What is its speed at this point?
   D. What is the coaster's maximum kinetic energy? Where is it? What is its speed at this point?
   E. What is the minimum electrical power which must be delivered for the coaster to complete one trip? Why is this a minimum?

For the past four years the wording of this question has been changed. The 1976, 1977 and 1978 versions lacked what now appears as parts A and B. Part A was added to require specifically that the student qualitatively discuss the energy transformations; part B was added to separate data taken from calculations required in parts C and D.

The particular criteria used in evaluating this question are represented by these questions:
   1. Is the work done on the system and subsequent energy transformations clearly explained?
   2. Is potential energy understood as a position function, i.e., that it requires the measurement of the vertical height?
   3. Is the transformation of potential energy into kinetic energy as the mass falls adequately described?
   4. Are dissipative forces described as doing work and requiring an energy input in each cycle?

One student in 1982 answered part A as follows:

"The coaster begins sitting still with no potential or kinetic energy. Then, the motor raises the coaster to the top of the first hill, thereby giving it a large amount of energy, most of which is potential. Then, the coaster goes through a series of other hills, but the total energy remains the same. However, the potential and kinetic energy constantly change. Then, at the end of the ride, the brakes slow the coaster down until its total energy is again zero. (Note that friction does take some energy from the coaster as it moves over the tracks.)"

In part E this student clarified his statement with: "It [referring to electrical energy] is the minimum because it must be used to get the coaster up the hill."

In estimating mass another student (1982) states:
"One coaster has twelve cars.

Each car weighs 440 lbs (estimate) 440 lbs = 200 kg.

Each car contains two people – 300 lbs = 140 kg.

Total mass of each car – 340 kg x 12 cars = 4080 kg."

This displays some confusion between mass and weight, kilograms and pounds.

As an example of measuring the vertical height of this ride, a student in 1981 did the following:

"There are 15 parallel crossbeams to the top of the highest hill. They are approximately 8 ft apart so the height is 120 ft (3 9 meters) approximately."

**Problem 3** applies to the Bumper Cars
A. Describe qualitatively the conservation or loss of momentum and energy for this ride.
B. Draw a momentum vector diagram of a single collision.
C. Find the change in momentum in a single collision. (vectors?!)
D. How does this ride operate? (HINT: Show a possible wiring diagram.)
E. Discuss the energy used by one car in one ride.

This fundamental question about conservation of momentum, conservation of energy and of energy transfer has appeared for each excursion to Six Flags. In an effort to improve clarity, the wording has undergone three revisions.

Student answers in 1976 led Page and Taylor to be particularly careful as the following year's class studied these topics, but our diligence did not yield any improvement in the 1977 papers. Continued diligence in succeeding years and attempts to improve wording have not yielded measurable improvement in student answers to this particular question.

Different wording, expectations, and graders have all influenced the year to year average. Nevertheless, comparisons of the better papers over these years seem to reflect decreasing understanding of conservation of momentum and energy in a collision. If such were the case for each of the Six Flags questions, it would indeed be alarming, however, only this particular question seems to display such a trend. Following is a comparison of two student answers; each of which were considered one of the best answers for that particular year.

A 1981 student writes,
"Momentum is conserved in this ride. Energy, however, is not conserved in the system. It is lost to heat and friction. Therefore, this ride consists of inelastic collision."

A 1977 student answered:
"Just as with colliding carts [reference to PSSC lab carts] each car has a momentum vector. When two collide the sum of the original momentum vectors equals the sum of the new momentum vectors. [A crude sketch was inserted at this point.] The same holds true for multicar collisions. The collisions are partially elastic. Much of the energy is dissipated as heat. Kinetic energy is *not* conserved."

The student then includes several sets of measure-

ments of distance and time from which speed and acceleration were calculated, and an estimate of the car's mass was made. The energy given to the car (assuming the car was "floored" the whole time) was computed.

In the last parts of this problem students often obtained current and voltage values from the ride operator. Here student ingenuity knew no bounds! In 1977 a group of students was observed hovering around a car tipped on its side. Close inspection found an operator – blueprint in hand – tracing the actual wiring of the car with the students. A crude wiring diagram is often included with a very general description to answer part D.

Here is a typical answer to part E by a 1981 student:
"Electrical energy is fed into the cart. The electrical energy is changed to mechanical energy in the motor, and then it is changed into kinetic energy to make the car move. Some of this kinetic energy is lost as heat during collisions."

The quality of answers to this part of the question has been fairly consistent.

In reading student responses to this question:
1. Many students think that momentum can be lost in the same manner as kinetic energy. Similarly, elasticity is often discussed in the context of momentum rather than energy.
2. The vector nature of momentum and vector addition is poorly understood.
3. There was often confusion or ignorance about the relationship between total mechanical energy conservation and the conservation of kinetic energy.
4. Roughly half the students were able either to correctly compute the electrical energy or at least to recognize that there was some relationship between the electrical energy and some computed mechanical energy.

As previously mentioned, course revisions have yet to yield improved student understanding as measured by this question. Yet we are encouraged that even a few have been able to make the "long haul" from estimated times and distances, classroom/laboratory/textbook equations and concepts, scrounged data from Six Flags personnel to some synthesis – however unsophisticated it might seem. Each fall presents a new opportunity for improvement in this area.

**Problem 4** applies to the Riverview Carousel (This is a large, restored, old fashioned Merry-Go-Round.)
This question applies to you *on the ride*.
A. What is your frequency about the axis of rotation?
B. What is your velocity?
C. What is your acceleration?
D. Draw a free-body diagram of the forces acting on you. Clearly identify *each* force. (Use an inertial reference frame.)
E. What is supplying the centripetal force?

This question has appeared on each year's exam. While parts A, B and C have remained almost unchanged, slightly different questions have appeared in parts D and E.

One of the better answers to A was presented in 1981:

"Period (sec) $F = 1/P$
1st lap 45 — The frequency for the first lap is .02
2nd lap 23 — rot/sec because it is accelerating. By the
3rd lap 23 — beginning of the 2nd lap, it is at full
4th lap 23 — speed and for the next four laps the $F =$
5th lap 23 — .04 rot/sec. The frequency for the last is
6th lap 45 — the same as the first. The average $F =$
.033 rot/sec."

Amusement Park Physics

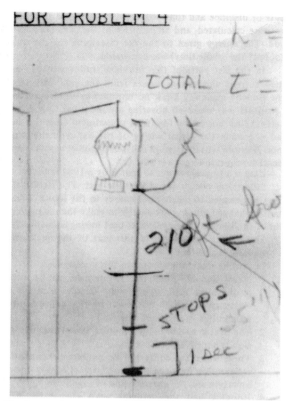

Fig. 5. A student's diagram of data for the Great Gasp, a controlled parachute drop.

Fig. 6. A student's paper.

Most students were not as thorough and instead took only a single measurement of time. To find the velocity required the radius and there was a number of students each year that did step off the circumference or attempt to directly measure the radius, but the majority read the sign and merely used that value. The following statement from a 1981 student was common, "The board here says that the circumference is 163 feet."

Many students knew the formula for calculating the speed; only a few remembered to specify the direction to give the velocity. Many had the correct equation for centripetal acceleration; only a few specified the direction. Many students were able to draw free-body diagrams to show the carousel horse pushing up, gravity pulling down, and a centripetal force "pushing" toward the center of the circle; only a few students specified the origin of the centripetal force.

### Problem 5

Problem: Make an estimate of one of the following: *Explain carefully how you arrived at your result.*

    A. The number of flowers on 4/23/77 at Six Flags

    B. The ratio of customers at Six Flags to the workers employed by Six Flags on 4/23/77.

    C. The change in the number of customers per hour at Six Flags on 4/23/77.

(This question, like some of the others, has changed from year to year. The motivation for change in this case, however, has been mostly to provide some surprises for the students.)

Many of us have heard or read the story about Enrico Fermi's question, "How many piano tuners are there in Chicago?" And there are, of course, many other stories about other great physicists' abilities to make almost incredibly fast estimations in place of complex calculation and to quickly determine the critical part of a complex system. This question represents an effort to encourage this sort of ability or skill.

Students were asked to choose between the three options above and the number choosing each is shown below:

| Choice | Frequency |
| --- | --- |
| A | 14 |
| B | 36 |
| C | 8 |

All the students working on the first choice computed a flower density, but some went from that figure directly to a map of Six Flags and then estimated the number of flower beds. Results ranged from 60 000 to 790 000 flowers. The lower figures are to be preferred simply because they seem to be associated with the papers that reflect the most care. (It is interesting that two groups of students working independently and with persistence found 60 000 and 73 000 respectively.)

Calculation of the customer to worker ratio was clearly the most popular question. No single good reason has been identified but several might be suggested.

    1. People are more interesting to count than flowers.

    2. There was the possibility of finding out some attendance figures that might at least provide a reasonable check point.

3. Gates have counters on them.

4. The main clusters of people were relatively few while there seemed to be flower beds nearly everywhere.

Since so many students worked on this choice, we were provided with a rich array of methods — some of them quite good — some unsatisfactory. Of course, there were two basic numbers that were necessary for computing the ratio: the number of employees and the number of visitors. One group presented the following information:

| Activity type | # of this type | Avg # empl. | Total employees |
|---|---|---|---|
| Rides | 25 | 5 | 125 |
| Stands | 21 | 2 | 42 |
| Shops | 48 | 4 | 192 |
| Unspecified | -- | - | 42 |
| Transportation | -- | - | 10 |
| Gate | 2 | 2 | 4 |
| | | | 415 |

To find the total number of customers in the park they wrote, "In an area about 1/15 of the park there were about 250 people = 15 x 250 = 3750 people in the park." Most papers showed values between 9:1 and 15:1.

The least popular counting question, was, we thought, the best question in that it contained the best of the second choice (interest, accessibility) and would still draw on all those fundamental laboratory skills we hopefully have been nurturing all year such as graphing, computing rates of change, selecting reasonable time intervals for frequency measurements, etc. At any rate, a few students did some interesting and good work with this problem.

The results of this particular question are most useful in evaluating the year-long laboratory experience specifically in terms of measurement because there is so little concept-dependent material here. In the bumper-car question, for example, many of the errors might stem from a poor "verbal" understanding of kinetic energy, but here the only concepts were those of counting and rates of change. We see need for improvement in the lab in the following areas.

1. The significance of a graph.
2. The concept of rate of change.
3. Clear definition of measuring procedures.

**Problem 6** applies to the Mind Bender
(The Mind Bender was put into operation in 1978 at Six Flags. It was advertised as the world's only triple-loop roller coaster. Two of the loops are in a vertical plane; the third loop is banked at 45 degrees.)

A. Show a free-body diagram of the forces acting on you when you are upside down. (Clearly identify *each* force.)

B. Why don't you fall out on your head?

C. What is the direction of the forces which you feel at this point when you are on this ride? Explain the agreement — or lack thereof — with your answer to part A. (Is the direction of the resultant force the same when viewed from the ground as when viewed/experienced from the ride?)

D. What is the minimum speed you can have (when upside down) and not fall out?

This problem has been included for only two years, but the concepts examined (frame of reference and the difference between centrifugal and centripetal forces) have been included on each trip to Six Flags.

A typical student's drawing is shown below.

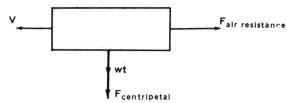

The student writes:

"You are held into your seat by centripetal force. Inertia causes your body wants to travel in a straight line, but the track pushes you to go into a loop, just as a rock on a string goes in a circle."

In his answer to C, he writes:

"When in the car, you feel a force pushing you into the seat while at the top of the loop. This force would be called centrifugal, an imaginary force introduced in an accelerated frame. This is different from A because of the accelerated frame of reference. The resultant force off of the ride is toward the center; on the ride it is away."

During the year the students saw Ivy and Hume's film "Frame of Reference." This film seems to be a great aid in helping visualize the difference between inertial and accelerated frames of reference. Still, this always presents a difficult subject for students to understand.

**Conclusion**

Any curious person looks for relationships to be used as predictors. Physics teachers are certainly no exception, so we were hoping that we might not only provide a good learning experience for our students, but also find out something about them that we didn't already know. However, there weren't any real surprises. Some "A" students didn't do as well as they expected, some "C" students with much tenacity did a little better than they expected.

We did observe the application of some essential survival skills that were a little surprising at first. The above-mentioned tenacity was one of those. Some students just wouldn't give up in spite of the unstructured and generally unhelpful environment. The second survival skill was communication. The open-book nature of the experience permitted and required meaningful verbal communication about physics. This ranged from two students discussing the definitions of weight and mass to a student's calling a hardware store to find out how many square feet a gallon of paint would cover. And we saw inventiveness at its best. With the restrictions imposed, new methods and tools were built and discovered. Some of this occurred as private insight and some as an entire group discovered a way to beat the perversity of one of our questions.

Finally, and most important, students were given an opportunity to be rewarded for reviewing physics in an environment totally different from their classroom. For most of them, the experience was pleasant yet demanding, different but still a test, and thorough but not a helpless ordeal. Each of us has learned some physics!

**Reference**

1. J. Roeder, Phys. Teach. **13**, 327 (1975).

Reprinted from *The Physics Teacher* **26**, 12-17, ©1988 American Association of Physics Teachers.

# Physics Students' Day at Six Flags/Magic Mountain

## By John McGehee

Every spring for the past six years a group of high school physics teachers from the Los Angeles area has organized a one-day event for high school physics students and prospective physics students at Six Flags/Magic Mountain, an amusement park on the outskirts of Los Angeles. The event has a dual purpose. First, it provides an opportunity for the students to put their classwork to practical use. Second, it serves to publicize physics to prospective students, with the hope of stimulating physics enrollment. Attendance has grown steadily from just under 2000 students and teachers representing around 100 schools the first year to 6000 from 220 schools participating this past year. This article will outline the various activities students are involved in on Physics Students' Day and the mechanics of organizing this type of an event.

### Overview of Student Activities

In advance of Physics Students' Day, participating teachers receive a packet of questions and problems involving the various rides at the park. To answer the questions the students must describe their motion or a sensation felt while on a particular ride. The problems require the students to measure or estimate the dimensions of a particular ride, time its motion, and calculate the speed and/or acceleration of a rider or some other physical quantity using their data. Some of the problems also require the direct measurement of a rider's acceleration for the purpose of comparing it with a calculated value. Hence, during the day much of the students' time is spent gathering data on selected rides and actually experiencing freefall, centripetal acceleration, and other phenomena discussed in their physics classes. Many of the problems can be found in one form or another in most high school physics texts, but it is hoped that they will take on a more "real-world" meaning when the actual physical situations are experienced in the context of having fun.

Another feature of Physics Students' Day is four Physics Olympics events in which the students can participate. Rules for the events are sent to the schools in one of the initial mailings. This gives the students an opportunity to practice the event prior to Physics Students' Day. Students may enter the events individually or in groups of two or three depending on the event. Trophies are given to the first and second place winners in each event.

### Mechanics and Organization

This version of amusement park physics grew out of a talk I gave about eight years ago at a local meeting of high school physics teachers describing a yearly trip to Six Flags/Magic Mountain for the purpose of gathering data to estimate speeds, accelerations, forces, etc.,

*John McGehee received his B.S. in Physics from UCLA and M.A. in Physical Science from California State University, Long Beach. After working in industry for several years, he began teaching physics at the high school level in 1966. He has taught PSSC and Project Physics in addition to the Advanced Placement Physics "C" course. John maintains contacts with industry by working as a physicist during summer vacations. In 1985, he received a Presidential Award for Excellence in Science Teaching (Rolling Hills High School, Rolling Hills Estates, CA 90274).*

experienced on the rides. After the talk a number of teachers got together and formed a group that is still the core of the Physics Students' Day organization committee. The committee currently consists of around 20 members and is divided into subcommittees of 3 to 5 members having responsibilities such as writing the rules for and supervising a Physics Olympics event or revising and editing problems.

The committee, along with a representative from the Six Flags organization, meets twice a year. The first meeting is usually in late November. At this time the date for the upcoming Physics Students' Day is chosen, Physics Olympics events and their locations in the park are decided upon, rules discussed, deadlines set, and a multitude of small details covered. The second meeting is held in the spring several weeks after the event. This meeting is primarily to critique the day and list changes and suggestions to be considered over the summer and fall until the next meeting. As one would imagine, the committee is made up of an enthusiastic, hardworking group of people.

During the early planning stages of the initial Physics Students' Day, the Six Flags organization treated the committee to a behind-the-scenes tour and provided an opportunity to discuss the rides with their engineering/maintenance staff. After the tour each committee member wrote a number of problems involving several rides. Those problems, along with problems involving rides subsequently installed at the park, form the basis of the problem packet. An example of the type of problems included in the packet is shown in Appendix A. These problems involve a ride called FREEFALL and are illustrative of the general type and level of problems included in the problem packet. The Six Flags engineering department supplied the committee with blueprints and data for the rides. These data are summarized in a "Data for Instructors Only" sheet.

Since the park security frowns upon students climbing over fences with tape measure in hand to make direct measurements of lengths, heights, etc., many of the quantities used in the problems must be estimated remotely using methods such as pacing or triangulation. To help teachers get their students started, a pamphlet entitled "Suggestions for Making Measurements" was written. The pamphlet outlines various techniques and describes simple instruments that can be used to make reasonable estimates of distances, speeds, and accelerations. A brief excerpt from the pamphlet is included in Appendix B.

Single copies of the problem packet, data sheet, and measurement pamphlet are mailed to all participating teachers. The teachers reproduce the problems and measurement pamphlet and supply copies to their students.

Each of the four Physics Olympics events is organized and run by a three- to five-member committee. Their responsibilities include writing the rules for the event, assembling any materials needed, and running and judging the event. At each event, the committee is usually aided in supervising by on-the-spot volunteer teachers.

At the outset there were many Physics Olympics events from which to choose.[1] In consultation with the Six Flags staff, four events were chosen for which there were appropriate locations in the park. These locations were reserved by the park staff on Physics Students' Day. For the first two years the events were the Paper Tower, Large Barge, Fermi Quiz, and Balsa Wood Bridge. The organizing committee decided that each year one event would require the construction of something in advance, e.g., a bridge. Materials for the other three events were to be supplied on site to participants.

Beginning in 1985, a fifth "demonstration" event was added. This event is open only to students of the organizing committee members. Its purpose is to demonstrate a new Physics Olympics event to the teachers and students. The following year this event replaces one of the previous events. For example, in 1985 the demonstration event was to build a car powered only by a particular size of rubber band. In 1986 it became one of the four events open to all students, replacing the Balsa Wood Bridge event. The next year the demonstration event was a paper airplane contest. It replaced one of the other three events in 1987. In this way teachers can become familiar with a variety of events and perhaps start a Physics Olympics within their school.

Over the years the Physics Olympics contests have become so popular that the number of entrants has had to be limited to the number that can be conveniently accommodated on a first-come, first-served basis. To reduce congestion on the part of spectators as well as participants, some events are scheduled simultaneously in different areas of the park.

In organizing an event of the magnitude of Physics Students' Day, the necessity of obtaining the thorough cooperation of the park management cannot be overstressed. Once convinced of the feasibility of Physics Students' Day, the Six Flags organization provided their enthusiastic support. It was desirable for the event to be staged at a time when attendance by the general public at the park was a minimum. Using the park attendance records, a Sunday in early March was chosen. An increase in attendance at such a time was also welcomed by park management. The first year Six Flags estimated that Physics Students' Day would result in an increase in attendance of about 500. When almost 2000 attended, they were convinced their support was justified. The fact that Physics Students' Day has been relatively easy to organize and trouble-free and has continued to grow is due in large part to the fine cooperation the committee receives from the management and staff at the park.

Support is provided by the park in various ways. There are three separate mailings prior to the day of the event. The first is in mid-December, announcing the upcoming Physics Students' Day. The second is in late January, again announcing the event. Included in the second mailing are publicity posters for school bulletin boards, ticket order forms,

**A student team assembles their paper tower during the "Paper Tower" Physics Olympics event.**

Physics Olympics event rules, and a sampling of problems from the problem packet. Around 700 public and private high schools receive these mailings. The third mailing goes out only to those ordering tickets. This mailing includes tickets, the complete problem packet, the "Suggestions for Making Measurements" pamphlet, the data sheet for teachers, and a letter reviewing details such as Physics Olympics event times, etc. The first and second mailings are handled entirely by the Six Flags staff and the third by the organizing committee. All printing and mailing costs are covered by the park. The

mailing list is maintained by the Six Flags organization and was compiled from a booklet produced by the organization that accredits high schools in California.

Advance-purchase tickets are provided by the park at a substantial discount to Physics Students' Day participants. They are placed on consignment with the organizing committee. Teachers from participating schools order the tickets from the committee by mail. The tickets are sent by return mail in advance of the event. After the event the unsold tickets and a check for the used tickets are mailed to the park. Part of the

**Students use a spring scale accelerometer to measure their acceleration while riding the BUCCANEER swinging ship.**

growth, both in overall attendance and in the number of schools participating. Much of its success is due to the careful thought and effort that has been put into the written materials provided to participants, the various activities, and the overall organization of the event by the organizing committee and the Six Flags staff. The results, along with the many positive comments from participating teachers, indicate that extra-classroom activities such as Physics Students' Day can be a useful motivational and learning tool within a high school physics program.

**Resource Material**

The event discussed here is just one approach to amusement park physics reported in *The Physics Teacher*. Others are described in references 2, 3, and 4.

A complete set of Physics Students' Day materials is available upon request.[5] These materials were specifically written for high school physics. The amusement park also has possibilities for other science courses. Carolyn Sumners has materials available that she and others have developed for the Informal Science Study project at the University of Houston. The materials describe amusement park activities for science students at a variety of grade levels.[6]□

motivation for providing discount tickets rests in the fact that the park does not have to handle the distribution of the tickets, which is a very time consuming task.

The park also provides much of the necessary logistical support in the form of audio equipment, signs around the park indicating locations and times of the various activities, and much of the equipment needed for the Physics Olympics events.

**Conclusion**

From its inception six years ago, Physics Students' Day at Six Flags/Magic Mountain has experienced a steady

**References**

1. David Riban, "Physics Olympics: Competitions for Secondary Physics Students," *Phys. Teach.* **14**, 471 (1976).
2. John Roeder, "Physics and the Amusement Park," *Phys. Teach.* **13**, 327 (1975).
3. George Taylor, Joseph Page, Murry Bentley, and Diane Lossner, "A Physics Laboratory at Six Flags Over Georgia," *Phys. Teach.* **22**, 361 (1984).
4. Kim Natale, "Final Exam in an Amusement Park," *Phys. Teach.* **23**, 228 (1985).
5. John McGehee, Rolling Hills High School, 27118 Silver Spur Road, Rolling Hills Estates, CA 90274, (213)377-0158 after 2 p.m.
6. Dr. Carolyn Sumners, Informal Science Study, University of Houston, Room 160, Farish Hall, Houston, TX 77004, (713)749-1692.

# Appendix A

## FreeFall

On FREEFALL, the rider boards the passenger pod at point A. The pod then travels with roughly constant speed from A to just below point B and then is brought to rest at point B. It then moves horizontally from B to C and is dropped from point C. Between C and D the pod and passengers are essentially in freefall. The pod then follows the circular path of radius R from points D to E. It then is decelerated between E and F and comes to rest at point G.

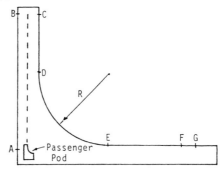

Measure or estimate the following distances

A to B = _____

C to D = _____

E to F = _____

R   = _____

Measure the following times:

t(A to B) = _____

t(C to D) = _____

t(E to F) = _____

The mass of a freefall passenger pod is about 680 kg. Assume the pod is loaded with four 60-kg physics students when answering questions where the total mass of the pod is needed. Using the data above, complete the following:

1. Calculate your average speed between points A and B in m/s and mph.

v(A to B) = _____ m/s = _____ mph.

2. Estimate the horsepower of the motor that lifts the loaded passenger pod from point A to B. List any simplifying assumptions that were made in arriving at your estimate.

_____

_____

_____

Power of motor = _____ hp.

3. Assuming you are freely falling between points C and D, calculate speed at point D in m/s and mph.

v(at D) = _____ m/s = _____ mph.

4. Assuming friction to be negligible between points D and E, calculate your speed at point E in m/s and mph.

v(at E) = _____ ms = _____ mph.

5. Calculate the maximum value of your acceleration between points D and E.

$\vec{a}_{max}$ = _____ , _____ .
           (magnitude)      (direction)

6. Find the magnitude and direction of the greatest centripetal force, $F_c$, experienced by the loaded passenger pod between points D and E.

$\vec{F}_c$ = _____ , _____ .
          (magnitude)      (direction)

7. Estimate the speed of the loaded pod at point F and use the Work–Energy theorem (Net Work = change in Kinetic Energy) and calculate the work done by friction as the pod moves from point E to F.

W(E to F) = _____ .

8. Calculate the average power dissipated as heat between points E and F.

$P_{ave}$(E to F) = _____ .

9. Find the average frictional force exerted on the pod between points E and F.

$F_{ave}$ = _____ .

10. Find the average value of your deceleration between points E and F.

$a_{ave}$ = _____ .

FREEFALL — Found only at Six Flags Magic Mountain!

## Appendix B

Following is an excerpt from the "Suggestions for Making Measurements" pamphlet describing the use of a spring scale as a simple accelerometer.

**Acceleration**

A simple device for measuring vertical accelerations (either up or down) is a 0-5 N spring scale with a 100-g mass attached. When measuring vertically upward accelerations such as at the bottom of the BUCCANEER, the spring scale is held vertically as in Fig. H. The forces on the mass are as drawn where $F_s$ is the reading on the scale. Applying Newton's second law,

$$F_s - mg = ma.$$

Thus the acceleration, a, of the mass (and also of the person holding the scale), is given by

$$a = (F_s - mg)/m = (F_s/m) - g.$$

If the person is holding the scale upside-down (for example, at the top of the rotation of the ENTERPRISE), the forces on m are as diagrammed in Fig. I. Again applying Newton's second law, the acceleration of the mass m is given by

$$a = - [(F_s/m) + g].$$

In either situation then, the acceleration can be calculated by knowing $F_s$.

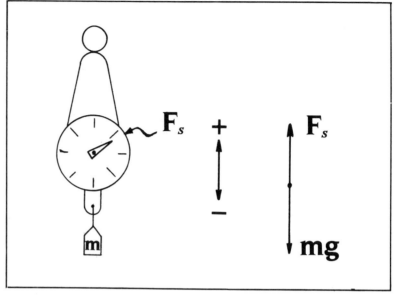

Fig. H. Forces on m when scale is "right side up."

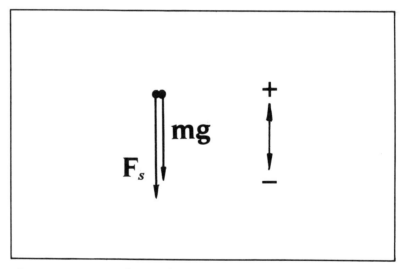

Fig. I. Forces on m when scale is "upside down."

THE PHYSICS TEACHER   JANUARY 1988   17